LE GESTIONNAIRE ET LES ÉTATS FINANCIERS

Passage aux normes internationales
NOTIONS DE BASE

D.-Claude Laroche

Louise Martel

Johanne Turbide

www.erpi.com/laroche.site

5757, RUE CYPIHOT, SAINT-LAURENT (QUÉBEC) H4S 1R3

TÉLÉPHONE: 514 334-2690 TÉLÉCOPIEUR: 514 334-4720

erpidlm@erpi.com www.erpi.com

ÉDITIONS DU RENOUVEAU PÉDAGOGIQUE INC.

D.-Claude Laroche (M.B.A., C.A.)
Professeur agrégé, HEC Montréal
Associé universitaire, Harel Drouin – PKF

Louise Martel (M. Sc., F.C.A.)
Professeure titulaire, HEC Montréal
Associée universitaire, KPMG

Johanne Turbide (Ph.D., M. Sc., C.A.)
Professeure agrégée, HEC Montréal

Pour la protection des forêts,
cet ouvrage a été imprimé sur
du papier recyclé

- contenant 100 % de fibres
  postconsommation;
- certifié Éco-Logo;
- traité selon un procédé
  sans chlore;
- certifié FSC;
- fabriqué à partir d'énergie
  biogaz.

FSC

BIO GAZ
ÉNERGIE

Développement de produits: Micheline Laurin
Supervision éditoriale: Sylvie Chapleau
Révision linguistique: Emmanuel Dalmenesche
Correction d'épreuves: Hélène Lecaudey

Direction artistique: Hélène Cousineau
Supervision de la production: Muriel Normand
Conception graphique de l'intérieur: Marie-Hélène Martel
Conception graphique de la couverture: Martin Tremblay
Édition électronique: Muriel Normand

Dépôt légal – Bibliothèque et Archives nationales du Québec, 2008
Dépôt légal – Bibliothèque et Archives Canada, 2008
Imprimé au Canada

1234567890   MI   098
20483 ABCD   ENV10

ISBN 978-2-7613-2626-1

Le but de cet addendum au manuel *Le gestionnaire et les états financiers* est de présenter un nouveau référentiel comptable appelé IFRS (pour *International Financial Reporting Standards*). Lorsqu'il sera introduit, en 2011, les sociétés ouvertes canadiennes (c'est-à-dire celles qui sont cotées en Bourse) devront adopter, en matière d'états financiers, des normes comptables conformes à cette pratique internationale qui suscite une adhésion de plus en plus large. Tout d'abord, nous présenterons dix changements significatifs qu'entraîneront ces normes internationales. Ensuite, nous mettrons ces changements en perspective. Enfin, nous approfondirons certains de ces points en expliquant leurs caractéristiques particulières. Pour plus de clarté, un glossaire établit une correspondance entre la terminologie actuelle et celle qui sera introduite avec l'utilisation des IFRS.

TABLE DES MATIÈRES

1. DIX POINTS SIGNIFICATIFS LIÉS AU PASSAGE AUX NORMES IFRS

Nous présentons ici, en dix points significatifs[1], les principaux changements qui toucheront l'interprétation des états financiers lorsqu'ils seront produits selon les normes IFRS. Ces changements sont décrits en fonction de la pratique actuelle des PCGR canadiens.

LE PASSAGE AUX NORMES IFRS

1. À propos du référentiel

L'introduction des normes IFRS amènera à utiliser un nouveau langage, ou «référentiel». Il s'agit des règles utilisées à la fois pour produire les états financiers et pour les interpréter. Jusqu'à présent, nous n'avions implicitement qu'un seul référentiel au Canada (les PCGR canadiens[2]); mais, dans un avenir prochain, il est possible que nous en ayons plusieurs, selon les secteurs ou types d'activités particuliers (par exemple, pour les organismes à but non lucratif ou les propriétaires exploitants). Pour le moment, les normes IFRS constitueront le référentiel pour les entités canadiennes ayant une obligation publique de rendre des comptes: sociétés cotées, certaines coopératives, institutions financières, maisons de courtage. La décision reste à venir pour ce qui est des autres référentiels qui seront utilisés.

• • • ▶

---

1. Pour des explications plus détaillées, voir la section 3.

2. Remarquons que les PCGR canadiens permettent à certaines entités (qui n'ont pas d'obligation publique de reddition de comptes) de produire des états financiers sans avoir à suivre certaines normes faisant partie des PCGR. On parle alors d'informations différentielles. Le terme «référentiel» n'est cependant pas utilisé, bien qu'il aurait pu l'être.

2. À propos de la forme des états financiers

Le cadre des IFRS définit des normes minimales devant être respectées, tout en laissant une certaine liberté pour ce qui est de la présentation des états financiers qui vont au-delà de ces normes. En vertu de certaines « traditions » ou « préférences culturelles », la forme des états financiers pourrait donc varier.

3 À propos du jeu d'états financiers concernant les capitaux propres

Le jeu d'états financiers exigé dans le cadre des IFRS et des PCGR canadiens est presque identique, à l'exception :

- de la présence de l'état de variation des capitaux propres, qui est exigé par les IFRS, alors qu'il a tendance à être facultatif au Canada ;
- et de l'existence d'un état des bénéfices non répartis pour les normes canadiennes, élément qui peut être intégré à l'état de variations des capitaux propres dans les IFRS.

4. À propos de l'état des résultats

Au Canada, il n'existe pas de format exigé pour l'état des résultats. En revanche, selon les IFRS, les charges doivent être présentées selon leur nature ou leur fonction. Notons également que les normes IFRS interdisent d'utiliser des postes extraordinaires, alors que cela est permis au Canada.

5. À propos des flux de trésorerie

L'état des flux de trésorerie est identique dans les deux jeux de normes, à l'exception du traitement du paiement des intérêts et des dividendes. Ceux-ci peuvent être présentés soit dans les opérations reliées à l'exploitation ou au financement (les montants versés sont alors associés à du financement), soit dans les opérations reliées à l'investissement (dans le cas de montants encaissés associés à des opérations d'investissement).

• • • ▶

6. À propos des immobilisations et des immobilisations incorporelles

L'interprétation du poste *Immobilisations* pourra donner lieu à deux enjeux :

- en raison de la nature plus précise des IFRS, il se peut qu'un poste d'immobilisations donne lieu à l'identification plus «détaillée» de ses diverses composantes, ce qui se traduira par des méthodes comptables d'amortissement plus «précises»;

- selon les IFRS, les immobilisations peuvent donner lieu à une réévaluation à la hausse de leur juste valeur, d'où une différence substantielle par rapport aux normes canadiennes, qui interdisent une telle pratique.

7. À propos des impôts futurs (ou impôts différés)

La lecture et l'analyse des états financiers seront différentes car, en vertu des normes IFRS, les impôts futurs (ou impôts reportés) sont tous considérés à long terme, alors qu'au Canada ils peuvent donner lieu à une portion présentée à court terme.

8. À propos des provisions et passifs éventuels

Les normes IFRS distinguent les passifs selon qu'ils sont constatés (à titre de provision) ou non constatés (passifs éventuels), pratique qui n'existe pas au Canada. Selon les normes IFRS, une provision à titre de passif (obligation légale ou implicite) peut être enregistrée aux états financiers si l'événement est considéré comme «plus probable» plutôt que comme «moins probable». Au Canada, on parle tout simplement de «probable», ce qui laisse penser que le niveau de probabilité exigé au Canada pour enregistrer une provision à titre de passif est plus élevé.

Les passifs éventuels (c'est-à-dire ceux qui ont moins de 50 % des chances de se réaliser) seront présentés dans les notes aux états financiers.

• • • ▶

9. À propos des participations des intérêts minoritaires, ou part des actionnaires sans contrôle

Il existe trois différences principales en matière de traitement des participations dans des filiales concernant la part des intérêts minoritaires (termes utilisés dans les IFRS), ou part des actionnaires sans contrôle (termes utilisés au Canada) :

– selon les IFRS, lors de l'acquisition d'une filiale, la part des intérêts minoritaires est présentée à la juste valeur de l'entreprise acquise, alors qu'au Canada elle l'est plutôt selon sa valeur comptable ;

– selon les IFRS, la part du bénéfice de la filiale qui est attribuée aux intérêts minoritaires est présentée dans la variation des capitaux propres, alors qu'au Canada on retrouve ce poste dans l'état des résultats ;

– selon les IFRS, la valeur des intérêts minoritaires est présentée au bilan comme partie intégrante des capitaux propres, alors qu'au Canada elle est présentée entre le passif et les capitaux propres.

10. À propos de l'étendue des informations à fournir

Les normes IFRS mettent l'accent sur la divulgation de l'information. Il faut donc s'attendre à ce que l'étendue des informations apparaissant aux états financiers soit plus importante que ce qui prévaut dans la pratique canadienne actuelle.

> « *Dans une logique de mondialisation des marchés des capitaux,
> les IFRS aideront les sociétés canadiennes à demeurer concurrentielles.* »
> Paul Cherry, président du Conseil des normes comptables du Canada
>
> Avril 2008[3]

LA RAISON D'ÊTRE DES NORMES INTERNATIONALES

Dans cette section, nous aborderons les enjeux suscités par l'introduction des normes internationales : le contexte de l'internationalisation des normes, l'évolution de la normalisation comptable et les modalités de passage aux normes IFRS.

2.1. L'internationalisation des normes de comptabilisation

Pourquoi des normes comptables internationales sont-elles nécessaires ? Une des explications tient à la mondialisation des affaires et des marchés des capitaux. En effet, en matière d'accès aux capitaux, les analystes doivent pouvoir faire des comparaisons et des analyses avec le moins de perturbations et de biais possible dans l'interprétation des données. Ainsi, les analyses auxquelles les entreprises procèdent avant de prendre des décisions d'investissement déboucheront sur un suivi plus aisé grâce à la clarté de la clef d'interprétation des données financières. De plus, de quelque pays qu'ils proviennent, les utilisateurs de l'information financière suivront un même ensemble de normes comptables, d'où une pertinence accrue de cette information d'un pays à l'autre.

Dans un article publié dans le *National Post*, abondamment cité par la suite, Paul Cherry, président du Conseil des normes comptables du Canada, exposait les raisons justifiant le passage aux normes IFRS au Canada. Parmi les arguments invoqués figuraient notamment les éléments exposés dans le tableau suivant[4].

---

3. *CA magazine*, avril 2008, p. 1.

4. *Financial Post*, mercredi 30 janvier 2008, repris dans *CA magazine*, avril 2008, p. 16-17.

Arguments en faveur de l'adoption des normes IFRS	Cherry 2008, extraits et adaptation
1. **L'adhésion mondiale aux IFRS**	« Le Canada ne peut rester à l'écart du mouvement d'acceptation grandissant d'une langue d'information financière commune. Le Canada ne représente même pas 4 % d'un marché financier devenu mondial. »
2. **Les coûts d'accès aux marchés des capitaux**	« Lorsque la langue comptable varie d'un pays à l'autre, les investisseurs ont du mal à comparer les sociétés entre elles, et ce sont eux finalement qui supportent le coût de la traduction. Avoir une langue comptable mondiale est la meilleure solution pour les sociétés ouvertes et les investisseurs. » « Les IFRS multiplieront les opportunités pour les entreprises canadiennes et leurs investisseurs, en abaissant le coût du capital, en facilitant l'accès aux marchés financiers internationaux et en éliminant la nécessité coûteuse des rapprochements. »
3. **Des normes comptables canadiennes jusqu'alors « ni blanches ni noires »... et la validité des normes IFRS**	« Nombre d'acteurs des marchés financiers canadiens étaient gênés des normes canadiennes ni blanches ni noires, c'est-à-dire ni conformes aux IFRS, ni conformes aux PCGR américains, mais composées d'un mélange des deux. » Ainsi, l'Organisation internationale des commissions de valeurs a jugé que les IFRS étaient « exhaustives, polyvalentes et susceptibles d'une interprétation et d'une application uniformes. [...] les IFRS constituent un mélange équilibré de principes généraux et de modalités d'application précises. »
4. **Au diapason d'une centaine de pays pour la prise de décision sur toile de fond mondiale**	« À l'heure où les entreprises prennent de plus en plus leurs décisions sur une toile de fond mondiale, le passage aux IFRS mettra le Canada au diapason d'une bonne centaine de pays, dont notamment ceux de l'Union européenne (à commencer par le Royaume-Uni) et l'Australie, ainsi que le Japon, la Chine, l'Inde, le Brésil, la Corée du Sud et Israël. »
5. **Une « approbation » des IFRS par la SEC (États-Unis) pour les émetteurs étrangers**	« À la fin de 2007, la Securities and Exchange Commission (SEC) a décidé de permettre aux émetteurs privés étrangers de déposer des états financiers établis selon les IFRS, au même titre que s'ils étaient établis selon les PCGR américains. Cela signifie que les sociétés canadiennes qui établiront leurs états financiers selon les IFRS ne seront plus tenues de rapprocher leurs états financiers des PCGR américains : une économie appréciable. »

Cependant, le passage aux normes IFRS exigera des efforts de la part des sociétés canadiennes et pourra entraîner des coûts importants pour certaines d'entre elles. À cet égard, on dit qu'il s'agit plus d'une course de fond que d'une course de vitesse[5].

---

5. Bellavance, C., *CA magazine*, avril 2008, p. 1.

2.2. L'influence des cultures – influences sociales et économiques

Le passage aux normes IFRS résulte d'un long processus au cours duquel divers courants d'influence se sont affrontés à propos de l'élaboration des normes comptables nationales de chaque pays et de leur contenu. Ainsi, dans les années 1980, différentes recherches[6] ont permis de distinguer les pays et de les regrouper en fonction de leurs différences «comptables». Parmi ces recherches, le schéma élaboré par Nobles permet de regrouper les pays selon que l'approche qu'ils suivent repose sur la microéconomie ou sur la macroéconomie uniforme[7].

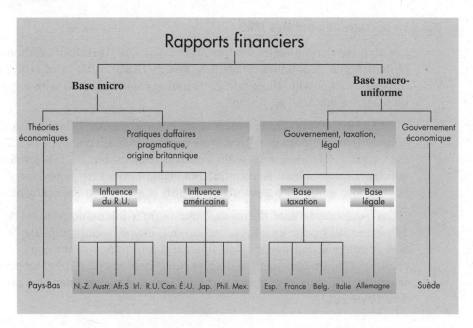

Ce schéma a permis d'opposer deux grands modèles de pays : le modèle franco-allemand (base macro-uniforme) et le modèle anglo-saxon (basé sur les pratiques d'affaires et l'approche pragmatique). À un extrême, on trouve une famille de pays influencée par une approche macro-uniforme dans laquelle le système comptable sert des objectifs économiques nationaux et contribue à l'élaboration de politiques nationales, et qui se caractérise par une grande uniformité dans la présentation de l'information, et ce, à des fins de compilation de

---

6. Par exemple, des illustrations apparaissent dans : Laroche, D.-C., *La comptabilité financière, la normalisation, les valeurs et l'état*, actes du colloque : Le comptable contemporain, professionnel de valeurs, HEC, 1985.

7. Dans Choi, F. D. S. et Mueller, G. G., *International Accounting*, Prentice-Hall, 1984.

statistiques, avec un cadre juridique qui impose un format standard de comptes et de règles (avec incidences fiscales). À l'autre extrême, on trouve des pays influencés par une approche microéconomique qui met l'accent sur les entreprises individuelles, privilégie l'élaboration de normes au cas par cas (pragmatisme), et dans laquelle on considère que les propriétaires d'entreprise sont les principaux destinataires des rapports.

On peut dire aujourd'hui que, en vertu de la primauté accordée aux besoins d'accès aux marchés des capitaux, les normes IFRS se sont développées dans un cadre influencé par le modèle anglo-saxon.

2.3. Le passage aux normes IFRS

Les normes internationales d'information financière (IFRS) sont élaborées par l'International Accounting Standards Board (IASB), dont la vocation est la suivante : « To provide the world's integrating capital markets with a common language for financial reporting[8]. »

L'IASB est l'organisme indépendant responsable de l'élaboration de ces normes. Il se compose de 14 membres provenant de divers domaines d'expertise et pays. L'IASB est la seule instance responsable de l'élaboration des normes. L'International Accounting Standards Committee Foundation (IASC Foundation) nomme les membres de l'IASB et assure son financement.

Au Canada, la date de passage aux normes internationales est fixée au 1er janvier 2011 pour les entreprises qui ont une obligation publique de reddition de comptes. Puisque les états financiers sont présentés sur une base comparative, il faudra également ajuster les états financiers de 2010 et les présenter selon les IFRS puisqu'ils feront partie intégrante des états financiers présentés à partir de 2011.

3. LES ÉTATS FINANCIERS

Dans cette section, nous examinerons plus en détail certains des éléments que nous avons relevés plus haut. Nous examinerons trois états financiers – l'état de la situation financière (ou bilan), l'état du résultat étendu (incluant l'état des résultats) et l'état des variations des capitaux propres – établis en fonction des normes comptables internationales. Nous ferons ressortir les différences entre ces états et les états financiers établis en fonction des normes comptables cana-

---

8. IASB, mars 2008, http://www.iasb.org/NR/rdonlyres/0A5A767C-E7DE-49E5-8B12-499F62F8870C/0/who_we_are.pdf

diennes, et ce, à l'aide des états financiers de la société française L'Oréal, qui œuvre essentiellement dans l'industrie du cosmétique.

Selon l'IASB, un jeu complet d'états financiers établis conformément aux normes comptables internationales comporte cinq composantes qui respectent les normes dans leur intégralité: l'état de la situation financière, l'état du résultat étendu, l'état des variations des capitaux propres, l'état des flux de trésorerie et les notes aux états financiers. Il est permis d'utiliser une terminologie différente de celle retenue dans les normes internationales pour autant que la compréhensibilité n'en soit pas affectée (voir le glossaire, page 21). La seule restriction est que chacun de ces états financiers soit clairement identifié afin que les utilisateurs puissent les reconnaître et les distinguer des autres informations contenues dans le rapport annuel.

3.1. L'état de la situation financière

Comme nous l'avons vu au chapitre 2 du manuel *Le gestionnaire et les états financiers*, le bilan exprime la situation financière de l'entreprise à une date donnée. Il n'est donc pas étonnant que l'IASB y fasse référence sous le nom d'«état de la situation financière». Cependant, les normes internationales n'obligent pas à adopter cet intitulé, et chaque entreprise peut choisir celui qui lui convient. D'ailleurs, plusieurs entreprises qui présentent leurs états financiers selon les normes internationales utilisent le terme «bilan», comme la société L'Oréal, tandis que certaines sociétés canadiennes cotées sur les marchés optent pour l'intitulé «état de la situation financière».

LA STRUCTURE ET LE CONTENU DE L'ÉTAT DE LA SITUATION FINANCIÈRE

L'état de la situation financière (ou bilan) présente ce que l'entreprise possède sous forme de biens et les sources du financement qu'elle a obtenu. Quoiqu'il s'agisse fondamentalement du même état que le bilan présenté au chapitre 2 du manuel, les normes internationales sont plus exhaustives quant aux composantes de l'état de la situation financière et à sa structure. Elles dressent ainsi[9] une liste des postes que devrait contenir tout état de la situation financière:

(a) immobilisations corporelles;

(b) immeubles de placement;

(c) immobilisations incorporelles;

(d) actifs financiers, à l'exclusion des montants indiqués en (e), (h) et (i);

(e) participations comptabilisées selon la méthode de la mise en équivalence[10];

---

9. IAS 1.

10. Selon les normes canadiennes, valeur de consolidation.

(f) actifs biologiques;

(g) stocks;

(h) clients et autres débiteurs;

(i) trésorerie et équivalents de trésorerie;

(j) fournisseurs et autres créditeurs;

(k) provisions;

(l) passifs financiers, à l'exclusion des montants indiqués en (j) et (k);

(m) passifs et actifs d'impôt exigible;

(n) passifs et actifs d'impôt différé;

(o) intérêts minoritaires, présentés au sein des capitaux propres;

(p) capital émis et réserves attribuables aux porteurs de capitaux propres de la société mère.

À l'exception des immeubles de placement et des actifs biologiques, on retrouve la plupart de ces postes dans les états financiers des sociétés canadiennes. Les immeubles de placement sont des biens immobiliers (par exemple un terrain ou un bâtiment) détenus dans le but de réaliser un produit de location ou une plus-value, c'est-à-dire un gain, à leur revente. On relève ici une différence avec la pratique canadienne, qui ne prescrit pas le traitement comptable de ce type d'actifs. Ainsi, au Canada, il est possible de trouver les immeubles de placement sous le poste *Placements* ou encore sous le poste *Immobilisations*.

Les actifs biologiques sont des actifs vivants tels que des plantes ou des animaux. Ce poste figure uniquement dans les états financiers des sociétés agricoles, et il existe des normes comptables réglementant leur comptabilisation. De telles normes n'existent pas au Canada.

Sauf exception, les normes internationales prescrivent de distinguer les actifs/passifs selon qu'ils sont à court ou à long terme, les qualifiant respectivement d'actifs/passifs courants et d'actifs/passifs non courants, comme c'est également le cas au Canada. Bien qu'elle ne soit pas obligatoire, la principale différence dans le mode de présentation des postes du bilan réside dans la structure même de l'état de la situation financière. Les normes internationales présentent, à titre d'exemple dans le texte normatif (voir le tableau ci-contre), un état de la situation financière qui classifie d'abord les postes d'actifs à long terme et conclut la section des actifs par le poste le plus liquide, soit la trésorerie, c'est-à-dire l'encaisse. De la même façon, la section de l'avoir et du passif présente d'abord l'avoir, puis le passif à long terme et enfin le passif courant. Au Canada, il est habituel de présenter les actifs par degré de liquidité décroissante et les passifs selon leur exigibilité.

EXEMPLE : Présentation selon les normes internationales

GROUPE XYZ – Bilan au 31 décembre 20X2
(En milliers d'unités monétaires)

	20X2	20X1
ACTIFS		
Actifs non courants		
Immobilisations corporelles	X	X
Goodwill	X	X
Autres immobilisations incorporelles	X	X
Participations dans des entreprises associées	X	X
Placements disponibles à la vente	X	X
Total des actifs non courants	X	X
Actifs courants		
Stocks	X	X
Clients	X	X
Autres actifs courants	X	X
Trésorerie et équivalents de trésorerie	X	X
Total des actifs courants	X	X
Total des actifs	X	X
CAPITAUX PROPRES ET PASSIFS		
Capitaux propres attribuables aux porteurs de capitaux propres de la société mère		
Capital social	X	X
Autres réserves	X	X
Résultats non distribués	X	X
Total (des capitaux propres attribuables aux porteurs de capitaux propres de la société mère)	X	X
Intérêts minoritaires	X	X
Total des capitaux propres	X	X
Passifs non courants		
Emprunts à long terme	X	X
Impôt différé	X	X
Provisions à long terme	X	X
Total des passifs non courants	X	X
Passifs courants		
Fournisseurs et autres créditeurs	X	X
Emprunts à court terme	X	X
Partie courante des emprunts à long terme	X	X
Impôt exigible à payer	X	X
Provisions à court terme	X	X
Total des passifs courants	X	X
Total des passifs	X	X
Total des capitaux propres et des passifs	X	X

C'est le mode de présentation retenu par L'Oréal (voir les extraits des états financiers de L'Oréal reproduits en appendice, p. 23-39). Comme on le remarque dans le bilan pour ce qui est des Actifs, L'Oréal présente d'abord les actifs non courants, puis les actifs courants, et, pour ce qui est des Capitaux propres et passifs, les capitaux propres, puis les passifs non courants et enfin les passifs courants.

On note deux autres différences entre l'état de la situation financière (normes internationales) et le bilan (normes canadiennes). En premier lieu, il s'agit de la terminologie : les termes utilisés peuvent en effet varier selon les pays francophones. En second lieu, il peut arriver que des différences de nature comptable persistent pour certains postes particuliers. Ci-dessous, nous tenterons de les expliquer dans la mesure où elles sont significatives pour le lecteur des états financiers.

Les stocks : définition et composantes

Les stocks d'une entreprise sont des actifs corporels destinés à la revente ou utilisés pour fabriquer les biens qui seront vendus. Les états financiers des entreprises commerciales et des entreprises de fabrication présentent généralement un poste *Stock* puisqu'elles vendent des biens qui doivent d'abord être achetés ou fabriqués. Cependant, pour une entreprise commerciale, le poste *Stock* représente le stock qu'elle a acheté mais non encore vendu, alors que, pour une entreprise de fabrication, il comprend généralement trois composantes à la date de fin d'exercice : les matières premières, les produits en cours et les produits finis.

Les matières premières représentent la matière dont une entreprise a besoin pour fabriquer le produit qu'elle vend. Par exemple, une entreprise qui fabrique des sofas a besoin de bois, de rembourrage et de tissu de recouvrement. Les produits en cours représentent les biens qui sont en voie de fabrication mais que l'entreprise n'a pas terminés à la date de fin d'exercice, soit la date de préparation de l'état de la situation financière. Ainsi, à la date de fin d'exercice, il est possible que l'entreprise précitée ait des sofas dont la base est terminée mais qui ne sont pas recouverts de tissu. Il s'agit des produits en cours. Enfin, les produits finis sont les biens qui sont complétés et offerts à la vente.

Les coûts d'acquisition des stocks – c'est-à-dire le coût de la matière première pour une entreprise de fabrication ou le coût d'acquisition des actifs destinés à la vente pour une entreprise commerciale – comprennent le prix d'achat, les droits de douane et autres taxes (autres que les taxes ultérieurement récupérables auprès des administrations fiscales), ainsi que les frais de transport, de manutention et autres coûts directement attribuables à l'acquisition des produits finis et des matières premières. Les rabais commerciaux, remises et autres éléments similaires sont déduits pour déterminer les coûts d'acquisition.

Le coût de fabrication, également appelé coût de transformation, comprend les coûts directement liés aux unités produites. Ainsi, les coûts directement liés aux sofas produits se composent du coût d'acquisition du bois et du coût de la main-d'œuvre. Le coût de fabrication comprend également des frais généraux de production qui sont engagés pour transformer les matières premières en produits finis. Ainsi, pour fabriquer des sofas, une entreprise a notamment besoin d'un local, d'équipement et d'électricité. Dans son coût de fabrication des sofas, elle doit donc inclure le coût lié à l'utilisation de la partie du bâtiment qui sert à la production des sofas. Ce coût est soit un loyer, si l'entreprise loue le bâtiment, soit l'amortissement, si elle est propriétaire du bâtiment.

Les méthodes de détermination du coût des stocks

Il existe trois grandes méthodes comptables pour déterminer le coût des stocks :

1. la méthode du coût propre ;
2. la méthode du coût moyen ;
3. la méthode de l'épuisement successif (FIFO).

L'entreprise doit choisir la méthode d'évaluation qui reflète le mieux sa conception de l'évolution des coûts de ses marchandises. Elle doit utiliser la même méthode pour tous les stocks de même nature et dont l'usage est similaire. Lorsqu'elle a déterminé celle qui lui convient le mieux, elle doit la conserver d'un exercice à l'autre tant que les circonstances ne justifient pas un changement. Par exemple, lorsqu'une entreprise en acquiert une autre qui utilisait une méthode différente, elle doit modifier l'une ou l'autre des méthodes de façon à utiliser une même méthode d'évaluation pour les stocks de même nature.

La valeur marchande des stocks

Une entreprise ne peut recouvrer le coût de ses stocks que si le prix de vente normal est supérieur à son coût d'acquisition ou de transformation. Lorsque la marchandise a été endommagée ou est devenue obsolète, ou lorsque son prix de vente a subi une baisse, l'entreprise peut se trouver dans l'incapacité de recouvrer les coûts qu'elle a engagés. C'est pourquoi les stocks sont évalués au moindre du coût et de la valeur nette de réalisation.

La valeur nette de réalisation est le prix de vente prévu dans le cas où les affaires suivent leur cours normal, moins les frais directs d'achèvement et de mise en vente. La pratique consistant à déprécier les stocks au-dessous du coût, pour les ramener à leur valeur nette de réalisation, est cohérente avec le principe suivant lequel les actifs ne doivent pas être comptabilisés à un montant supérieur au montant qu'on s'attend à obtenir de leur vente ou de leur utilisation.

Si la valeur d'un stock diminue et atteint seulement la valeur nette de réalisation, on dira que le stock est déprécié, et une charge correspondant à cette dépréciation sera inscrite à l'état des résultats. Si un stock déprécié voit sa valeur augmenter, la dépréciation doit être annulée jusqu'à concurrence du coût initial, sans le dépasser.

Les placements dans les coentreprises et les satellites

Au Canada, les participations dans des coentreprises sont comptabilisées selon une seule méthode : la consolidation proportionnelle. Les normes internationales, elles, permettent deux modes de comptabilisation pour ces placements :

- la consolidation proportionnelle ; et
- la mise en équivalence, appelée « valeur de consolidation » au Canada.

L'IASB accorde cependant sa préférence à la consolidation proportionnelle.

Selon les normes internationales, un placement dans un satellite correspond aux participations dans des entreprises associées. Elles en donnent une définition équivalente : un placement dans une entreprise sur laquelle l'investisseur exerce une influence notable.

Les immobilisations corporelles et incorporelles

Selon les normes internationales, comme au Canada, les immobilisations corporelles sont évaluées initialement au coût. Le coût comprend toutes les dépenses encourues pour permettre l'utilisation de l'immobilisation. Lorsque l'entreprise a des frais de décontamination ou de restauration des lieux à la fin de la vie utile d'une immobilisation, elle doit ajouter ces frais au coût initial de l'immobilisation. Par ailleurs, les normes internationales exigent l'adoption de l'approche par composantes. Ainsi, lorsqu'une entreprise acquiert une immobilisation dont les composantes importantes ont des durées de vie différentes, elle doit scinder le coût d'acquisition de l'immobilisation pour tenir compte de ces durées de vie différentes et amortir chacune des composantes selon la méthode qui reflète le mieux sa durée de vie utile. Par exemple, une entreprise qui achète un avion commercial devra amortir la carlingue, les moteurs et les équipements en utilisant différents taux ou méthodes.

Selon les normes internationales, une entreprise doit déterminer la méthode de comptabilisation qu'elle retiendra pour chaque catégorie d'immobilisations, une fois inscrit le coût d'acquisition. Deux modèles d'évaluation sont permis : le *modèle du coût* et le *modèle de la réévaluation* (évaluation à la juste valeur). Pour chaque catégorie d'immobilisations, l'entreprise doit faire un choix entre ces deux modèles et s'y tenir, à moins que les circonstances justifient un changement.

Les normes internationales privilégient le modèle du coût, se rapprochant ainsi des normes canadiennes. Par ailleurs, selon les IFRS, il est possible de réduire la dépréciation d'une immobilisation prise antérieurement ou de l'annuler. Ainsi, un terrain dont le coût était de 300 000 $ et qui a été déprécié à 100 000 $ (une charge de 200 000 $ à l'état des résultats) pourrait, dans un exercice ultérieur, retrouver jusqu'à sa valeur initiale de 300 000 $ (produit à l'état des résultats), mais sans jamais dépasser ce coût initial. Cette pratique n'est pas acceptée au Canada pour les immobilisations.

Une entreprise peut également choisir le modèle de la réévaluation pour une ou plusieurs catégories d'immobilisations, tant corporelles qu'incorporelles, pour autant qu'il soit possible d'en mesurer la juste valeur. Évidemment, la nouvelle valeur doit être justifiée et fondée sur la valeur de réalisation telle qu'elle est déterminée par des experts indépendants ou à partir de valeurs de remplacement si elles existent. Mesurer la juste valeur d'un actif incorporel se révèle souvent une tâche difficile. C'est pourquoi les normes internationales précisent qu'on ne peut mesurer la valeur de tels actifs que s'il existe un marché actif où se négocient ces biens.

La réévaluation doit être appliquée à l'ensemble des biens d'une même catégorie et non à une immobilisation isolément. De plus, cette réévaluation doit être pratiquée périodiquement en fonction de l'importance des fluctuations de valeur, et ce, afin que le montant présenté à l'état de la situation financière ne diffère pas significativement de la juste valeur desdites immobilisations. La valeur réévaluée fait l'objet d'un amortissement comme si l'immobilisation avait été comptabilisée au coût historique. L'*écart de réévaluation* ainsi que la *fraction de l'amortissement liée à la plus-value* seront comptabilisés en tant que postes distincts à l'état des variations des capitaux propres.

Une entreprise qui investit dans un immeuble de placement doit comptabiliser ces investissements dans un poste distinct à l'état de la situation financière. Un immeuble de placement est un bien immobilier détenu dans le but d'en retirer des produits de location ou de réaliser une plus-value, c'est-à-dire un gain, à la revente. Un immeuble de placement est initialement comptabilisé au coût. Par la suite, l'entreprise doit décider de comptabiliser cet immeuble de placement soit au coût amorti, soit à la juste valeur. Ce choix doit être identique pour tous les immeubles de placement qu'elle détient. Lorsque l'entreprise opte pour la juste valeur, les variations de juste valeur sont comptabilisées directement à l'état des résultats. Comme nous l'avons mentionné précédemment, les normes internationales exigent que les immeubles de placement soient présentés de façon distincte à l'état de la situation financière. Une telle norme n'existe pas au Canada.

Les provisions et les passifs éventuels

Une provision est une dette dont l'échéance ou le montant est incertain. Il s'agit d'une situation qui entraînera probablement un déboursé dans le futur. Une entreprise doit donc comptabiliser un passif, appelé *provision pour risques et charges*, quand :

- à la date du bilan, elle a une obligation juridique ou implicite résultant d'un fait passé ;
- il est probable qu'elle doive se départir de ressources, principalement de l'argent, pour régler cette obligation ;
- elle peut estimer le montant de façon fiable.

Le bilan de L'Oréal illustre la comptabilisation d'une provision pour risques et charges de 148,5 millions d'euros, accompagnée de renseignements supplémentaires dans la note 22 aux états financiers (voir page 37).

Ainsi, au Canada, même s'il n'existe pas de norme spécifique en matière de comptabilisation des provisions, il est courant que de tels postes figurent aux états financiers, comme nous l'avons mentionné au chapitre 2 du manuel. On peut penser que la comptabilisation des provisions est à peu près identique, qu'on suive les normes internationales ou la pratique canadienne. La différence réside toutefois dans l'interprétation qu'on donne de la probabilité que l'entreprise soit tenue de régler l'obligation. En effet, le référentiel international est beaucoup plus explicite à cet égard.

- Si l'obligation ne répond pas aux trois conditions mentionnées ci-dessus, ce passif est considéré comme un passif éventuel. Contrairement à une provision, un passif éventuel est un événement non comptabilisé, c'est-à-dire qu'il est divulgué uniquement par le biais d'une note aux états financiers. Selon les normes internationales, un passif éventuel est principalement une obligation résultant d'événements passés mais qui ne donnent pas lieu à la constitution d'un passif :
- soit parce que l'entreprise ne juge pas probable qu'elle doive se départir de ressources, c'est-à-dire qu'il y a selon elle moins de 50 % des chances que l'événement donnant lieu au passif se réalise ;
- soit, dans de rares cas, parce que l'entreprise n'est pas en mesure d'estimer le montant de la provision avec suffisamment de fiabilité.

3.2. L'état du résultat étendu

Le résultat étendu représente la variation des capitaux propres qui proviennent des transactions ou autres événements qui se sont produits au cours de la période, à l'exception des transactions qui ont eu lieu directement avec les propriétaires/actionnaires, à titre de propriétaires, comme le versement de dividendes.

À compter du 1er janvier 2009[11], les sociétés ayant adopté les normes internationales seront tenues d'appliquer les recommandations de la nouvelle norme de présentation des états financiers que nous abordons ici. Cette norme impose aux entreprises de produire un état du résultat étendu, comme elles sont tenues de le faire au Canada depuis le 1er octobre 2006.

Selon les normes internationales, les entreprises peuvent présenter leurs états financiers de deux façons. Elles pourront présenter :

■ soit deux états distincts, c'est-à-dire un état des résultats et un état du résultat étendu (voir l'exemple 1 ci-dessous) ;

■ soit un seul état du résultat étendu, combinant l'état des résultats et l'état du résultat étendu (voir l'exemple 2 page suivante).

EXEMPLE 1 : Deux états distincts : un état des résultats et un état du résultat étendu

ÉTAT DES RÉSULTATS

Produits	100
Coûts des ventes	50
Marge brute	50
Charges de vente et d'administration	20
Résultat avant impôts	30
Impôts	10
Résultat net	20
Résultat net attribuable aux propriétaires	16
Résultat net attribuable aux actionnaires minoritaires	4

ÉTAT DU RÉSULTAT ÉTENDU

Résultat net	20
Autres éléments du résultat étendu, après impôts :	
Gains/Pertes sur réévaluation d'actifs corporels	4
Gains/Pertes de change latents sur conversion des états financiers d'établissements étrangers autonomes	(2)
Résultat étendu	22
Résultat étendu attribuable aux propriétaires	17,6
Résultat étendu attribuable aux actionnaires minoritaires	4,4

---

11. C'est pour cette raison que L'Oréal ne présente pas d'état du résultat étendu.

EXEMPLE 2 : Un seul état du résultat étendu, combinant l'état des résultats et l'état du résultat étendu

ÉTAT DU RÉSULTAT ÉTENDU

Produits	100
Coûts des ventes	50
Marge brute	50
Charges de vente et d'administration	20
Résultat avant impôts	30
Impôts	10
Résultat net	20
Autres éléments du résultat étendu, après impôts :	
Gains/Pertes sur réévaluation d'actifs corporels	4
Gains/Pertes de change latents sur conversion des états financiers	
d'établissements étrangers autonomes	(2)
Résultat étendu	22
Résultat étendu attribuable aux propriétaires	17,6
Résultat étendu attribuable aux actionnaires minoritaires	4,4

L'ÉTAT DES RÉSULTATS

Non seulement les normes internationales exigent qu'un minimum de postes soit présenté à l'état des résultats, mais elles prescrivent également deux types de présentation des charges à l'état des résultats, selon :

- soit la nature des charges, ce qu'on appelle la méthode des charges par nature, c'est-à-dire en ventilant les charges selon qu'elles représentent la consommation de matières premières, les salaires, l'amortissement, etc. ;
- soit la fonction des charges au sein de l'entreprise, ce qu'on appelle la méthode des charges par fonction ou méthode « du coût des ventes », c'est-à-dire en ventilant les charges selon leur fonction, par exemple charges de publicité, charges de distribution, charges administratives, etc.

Comme cela a été décrit au chapitre 2 du manuel, les normes comptables canadiennes exigent de toutes les sociétés qu'elles présentent un minimum de postes à leur état des résultats, mais elles leur permettent d'établir cet état de plusieurs manières, selon qu'on veut présenter l'information par blocs de produits et charges ou fournir plus de détails sur chaque catégorie de produits et charges. Ainsi, le mode de présentation de l'état des résultats, particulièrement en ce qui a trait aux sous-totaux retenus, varie d'une entreprise à l'autre en fonction des choix de l'entreprise.

La méthode des charges par nature

Selon les normes internationales, voici à quoi ressemblerait un état des résultats présentés selon la méthode des charges par nature.

Produit des activités ordinaires		X
Autres produits		X
Variations des stocks de produits finis et des travaux en cours	X	
Matières premières et consommables utilisées	X	
Coût des avantages du personnel	X	
Dotations aux amortissements	X	
Autres charges	X	
Total des charges		(X)
Résultat		X

La méthode des charges par fonction

La méthode des charges par fonction, également appelée méthode du «coût des ventes», ressemble à celle qu'on retrouve au Canada. Selon les normes internationales, une société qui opte pour cette présentation doit en outre ventiler certaines de ses charges présentées par fonction d'après leur nature, en donnant cette information supplémentaire par le biais de notes aux états financiers. Par exemple, l'amortissement est réparti dans plusieurs postes de nature différente, comme les charges administratives et le coût des ventes. C'est pour cette raison que les normes internationales exigent de plus que les sociétés divulguent, à titre d'information supplémentaire, la dépréciation, l'amortissement ainsi que les charges liées au personnel. C'est de cette façon que L'Oréal, par exemple, présente les notes sur les charges liées au personnel et à l'amortissement (voir les pages 34 et 35).

Selon cette méthode, les entreprises doivent en outre présenter au minimum le poste *Coût des ventes*, ce qui ne correspond pas à la pratique actuelle au Canada. Depuis le 1er janvier 2008, les sociétés canadiennes doivent cependant présenter le poste relatif aux charges liées aux stocks (soit le coût des ventes) de façon distincte dans l'état des résultats.

Voici un exemple d'état des résultats présenté selon la méthode des charges par fonction, comme cela est prescrit dans les normes internationales.

Produit des activités ordinaires	X
Coût des ventes	(X)
Marge brute	X
Autres produits	X
Coûts commerciaux	(X)
Charges administratives	(X)
Autres charges	(X)
Résultat	X

L'Oréal a opté pour ce type de présentation de l'état des résultats (voir les extraits des états financiers de L'Oréal reproduits en appendice, p. 23-39).

Enfin, une autre différence entre les normes canadiennes et internationales tient à la présentation des charges. La notion de poste extraordinaire n'existe pas dans les normes internationales, qui précisent cependant qu'une entreprise doit présenter dans un poste distinct tout produit ou charge dont le montant ou la nature est significatif. Les normes internationales offrent les exemples suivants de ce qui pourrait correspondre à la notion de poste significatif:

■ dépréciation de stock ou d'actif immobilisé;
■ frais de restructuration;
■ gain/perte à la sortie d'immobilisations corporelles;
■ gain/perte à la vente de placement;
■ activités abandonnées;
■ règlement de litige;
■ reprise de provision.

3.3. L'état des variations des capitaux propres

Parmi les composantes de la section «Capitaux propres» au bilan, on retrouve:

■ le capital-actions;
■ les résultats non distribués ou bénéfices non répartis (BNR);
■ le cumul des autres éléments du résultat étendu.

L'état des variations des capitaux propres sert à renseigner les utilisateurs sur les changements survenus au sein de chacune de ces composantes au cours de la période. Il présente ainsi les variations du capital-actions (émissions ou rachat), les variations des résultats non distribués, (c'est-à-dire le résultat de l'exercice et les dividendes versés), ainsi que les variations de chacun des éléments du résultat étendu. Cet état doit également présenter la part des capitaux propres qui appartient aux actionnaires sans contrôle, autrement dit les intérêts minoritaires.

Cet état inclut l'état des bénéfices non répartis qu'il remplace. L'état des variations des capitaux propres, plus complet, est généralement présenté sous la forme d'un tableau à plusieurs colonnes ; il comprend à la fois les éléments de l'état des bénéfices non répartis, comme le résultat net et les dividendes, et les variations des autres composantes du résultat étendu, ainsi que les variations du capital-actions.

Nous présentons à la page 22 un exemple de l'état des variations des capitaux propres donné dans les normes internationales. En ce qui concerne L'Oréal, on remarquera que certaines informations ont été combinées dans la colonne « Éléments constatés directement en capitaux propres ».

4. GLOSSAIRE – ÉQUIVALENCES ENTRE LA TERMINOLOGIE CANADIENNE ET LA TERMINOLOGIE INTERNATIONALE

Termes ICCA Financiers canadiens	Termes IFRS
Actifs à court terme	Actifs courants
Actifs à long terme	Actifs non courants
Placements dans les sociétés satellites	Participations dans les entreprises associées
Immobilisations	Immeubles de placement
Écart d'acquisition	Goodwill
Impôt futurs	Impôts différés
Passif à court terme	Passifs courants
Impôts à payer	Dette d'impôt exigible
Passif à long terme	Passifs non courants
Passif au titre des prestations de retraite constituées	Provision pour retraites
Capital-actions	Capital
Part des actionnaires sans contrôle	Intérêts minoritaires
	Résultat net, part du groupe
Avantages sociaux futurs	Avantages liés au personnel
Valeur de consolidation	Méthode de mise en équivalence
Satellite	Entité associée
Éventualités	Passifs éventuels
Information sectorielle	Segments opérationnels
Opérations entre apparentées	Informations relatives aux parties liées

EXEMPLE: État des variations des capitaux propres

GROUPE XYZ
État des variations des capitaux propres pour l'exercice clos le 31 décembre 20X2
(En milliers d'unités monétaires)

| | Attribuables aux porteurs de capitaux propres de la société mère | | | | | | | | |
	Capital social	BNR	Écarts de conversion	Actifs financiers disponibles à la vente	Couvertures de trésorerie	Surplus de réévaluation	Total	Intérêts minoritaires	Total des capitaux propres
Solde au 1er janvier 20X1	X	X	(X)	X	X	–	X	X	X
	–	X	–	–	–	–	X	X	X
Changements … 20X1									
Dividendes	–	(X)	–	–	–	–	(X)	–	(X)
Total	–	X	X	X	X	X	X	X	X
Solde au 31 décembre 20X1	X	X	X	X	(X)	X	X	X	X
Changements … 20X2	X	–	–	–	–	–	–	–	X

APPENDICE

Extraits des comptes consolidés de L'ORÉAL

COMPTES DE RÉSULTAT CONSOLIDÉS COMPARÉS

En millions d'euros

	2007	2006	2005
Chiffre d'affaires (note 3)	**17 062,6**	**15 790,1**	**14 532,5**
Coût des ventes	-4 941,0	-4 569,1	-4 347,3
Marge brute	**12 121,6**	**11 221,0**	**10 185,2**
Frais de recherche et développement	-559,9	-532,5	-496,2
Frais publipromotionnels	-5 126,7	-4 783,0	-4 367,2
Frais commerciaux et administratifs	-3 618,2	-3 309,4	-3 009,3
Résultat d'exploitation avant pertes et gains de change	**2 816,8**	**2 596,1**	**2 312,5**
Pertes et gains de change (note 6)	10,4	-55,2	-46,5
Résultat d'exploitation	**2 827,2**	**2 540,9**	**2 266,0**
Autres produits et charges (note 7)	621,6	-60,8	9,3

Résultat opérationnel	**3448,8**	**2480,1**	**2275,3**
Coût de l'endettement financier net (note 8)	-174,5	-115,9	-63,8
Autres produits et charges financiers	-7,6	-3,6	-3,3
Dividendes Sanofi-Aventis	250,3*	217,4	171,6
Quote-part du résultat net des sociétés mises en équivalence	0,1	-1,2	-0,7
Résultat avant impôt	**3517,2**	**2576,8**	**2379,1**
Impôts sur les résultats (note 9)	-859,7	-514,7	-405,9
Résultat net	**2657,5**	**2062,1**	**1973,2**
Dont :			
- part du groupe	2656,0	2061,0	1972,3
- part des minoritaires	1,5	1,1	0,9
Résultat net par action part du groupe (euros) (note 10)	4,42	3,36	3,13
Résultat net dilué par action part du groupe (euros) (note 10)	4,38	3,35	3,13
Résultat net par action hors éléments non récurrents part du groupe (euros) (note 10)	3,39	2,99	2,60
Résultat net dilué par action hors éléments non récurrents part du groupe (euros) (note 10)	3,36	2,98	2,60

BILANS CONSOLIDÉS COMPARÉS

En millions d'euros

Actif	31.12.2007	31.12.2006	31.12.2005
Actifs non courants	**16 979,6**	**19 155,4**	**18 686,0**
Ecarts d'acquisition (note 11)	4344,4	4053,9	3837,1
Autres immobilisations incorporelles (note 12)	1959,2	1792,8	1201,0
Immobilisations corporelles (note 14)	2651,1	2628,4	2466,0
Actifs financiers non courants (note 15)	7608,9	10168,5	10757,1
Titres mis en équivalence	–	82,0	–
Impôts différés actifs (note 9)	416,0	429,8	424,8
Actifs courants	**6 220,7**	**5 627,6**	**5 200,1**
Stocks (note 16)	1547,6	1404,4	1261,8
Créances clients (note 17)	2617,5	2558,5	2379,7
Autres actifs courants (note 18)	926,4	851,8	829,0
Impôts sur les bénéfices	42,5	31,7	66,4
Trésorerie et équivalents de trésorerie (note 19)	1086,7	781,2	663,2
Total de l'actif	**23 200,3**	**24 783,0**	**23 886,1**

Passif	31.12.2007	31.12.2006	31.12.2005
Capitaux propres (note 20)	**13 621,8**	**14 624,2**	**14 657,2**
Capital	123,6	127,9	131,7
Primes	963,2	958,5	953,9
Autres réserves	8695,8	8974,4	8824,8
Eléments constatés directement en capitaux propres	3408,9	5066,9	5197,2
Réserve de conversion	−441,1	−70,3	214,0
Actions autodétenues	−1787,2	−2496,3	−2638,2
Résultat net part du groupe	2656,0	2061,0	1972,3
Capitaux propres - part du groupe	**13 619,2**	**14 622,1**	**14 655,7**
Intérêts minoritaires	2,5	2,1	1,5
Passifs non courants	**3 978,5**	**3 396,9**	**2 460,5**
Provisions pour retraites et autres avantages (note 21)	755,3	837,9	960,6
Provisions pour risques et charges (note 22)	148,5	154,1	−157,0
Impôts différés passifs (note 9)	491,6	512,5	914,7
Emprunts et dettes financières non courants (note 23)	2583,0	1892,4	428,2
Passifs courants	**5 600,1**	**6 761,9**	**6 768,4**
Dettes fournisseurs	2528,7	2485,0	2276,5
Provisions pour risques et charges (note 22)	285,7	272,0	289,3
Autres passifs courants (note 25)	1732,5	1613,9	1523,2
Impôts sur les bénéfices	176,5	173,0	227,3
Emprunts et dettes financières courants (note 23)	876,8	2218,0	2452,1
Total du passif	**23 200,3**	**24 783,0**	**23 886,1**

TABLEAU DE VARIATION DES CAPITAUX PROPRES CONSOLIDÉS

En millions d'euros

	Nombre d'actions en circulation	Capital	Primes	Autres réserves et résultat	Eléments constatés directement en capitaux propres	Actions auto-détenues	Réserves de conversion	Capitaux propres part du groupe	Intérêts minoritaires	Capitaux propres
Situation au 31.12.2004	638 274 360	135,2	953,5	10295,3	3031,0	−2450,9	−139,9	11 824,2	1,2	11 825,4
Augmentation de capital	7500	0,0	0,4					0,4		0,4
Annulation d'actions autodétenues		−3,5		−980,9		984,4				
Dividendes versés (hors actions propres)				−518,8				−518,8	−0,6	−519,4
Réserves de conversion							353,9	353,9	0,2	354,1
Actifs financiers disponibles à la vente					2255,8			2255,8		2255,8
Couverture des flux de trésorerie					−89,6			−89,6	−0,1	−89,7
Variations reconnues directement en capitaux propres					2166,2		353,9	2520,1	0,1	2520,2
Résultat consolidé de l'exercice				1972,3				1972,3	0,9	1973,2
Total des produits et charges comptabilisés				1972,3	2166,2		353,9	4492,4	1,0	4493,4
Rémunérations payées en actions				29,9				29,9		29,9

	Nombre d'actions	Capital	Primes			Actions propres		Capitaux propres part du Groupe	Intérêts minoritaires	Capitaux propres totaux
Variation nette des titres L'Oréal autodétenus	-18 308 250			-0,9		-1 171,7		-1 172,6		-1 172,6
Autres variations				0,2				0,2	-0,1	0,1
Situation au 31.12.2005	619 973 610	131,7	953,9	10 797,1	5 197,2	-2 638,2	214,0	14 655,7	1,5	14 657,2
Augmentation de capital	76 000	0,0	4,6					4,6		4,6
Annulation d'actions autodétenues		-3,8		-1 255,6		1 259,4		—		—
Dividendes versés (hors actions propres)				-616,1				-616,1	-0,9	-617,0
Réserves de conversion							-284,3	-284,3	0,2	-284,1
Actifs financiers disponibles à la vente					-194,5			-194,5		-194,5
Couverture des flux de trésorerie					64,2			64,2		64,2
Variations reconnues directement en capitaux propres					-130,3		-284,3	-414,6	0,2	-414,4
Résultat consolidé de l'exercice				2 061,0				2 061,0	1,1	2 062,1
Total des produits et charges comptabilisés				2 061,0	-130,3		-284,3	1 646,4	1,3	1 647,7
Rémunérations payées en actions				49,4				49,4		49,4
Variation nette des titres L'Oréal autodétenus	-14 327 500			-1,5		-1 117,5		-1 119,0		-1 119,0
Autres variations				1,1				1,1	0,2	1,3
Situation au 31.12.2006	605 722 110	127,9	958,5	11 035,4	5 066,9	-2 496,3	-70,3	14 622,1	2,1	14 624,2

TABLEAU DE VARIATION DES CAPITAUX PROPRES CONSOLIDÉS (suite)

En millions d'euros

	Nombre d'actions en circulation	Capital	Primes	Autres réserves et résultat	Eléments constatés directement en capitaux propres	Actions auto-détenues	Réserves de conversion	Capitaux propres part du groupe	Intérêts minoritaires	Capitaux propres
Situation au 31.12.2006	**605722110**	**127,9**	**958,5**	**11035,4**	**5066,9**	**−2496,3**	**−70,3**	**14622,1**	**2,1**	**14624,2**
Augmentation de capital	75050	−	4,7					4,7		4,7
Annulation d'actions autodétenues		−4,3		−1704,8		1709,1		−		−
Dividendes versés (hors actions propres)				−711,6				−711,6	−0,9	−712,5
Réserves de conversion							−370,8	−370,8		−370,8
Actifs financiers disponibles à la vente					−1685,9			−1685,9		−1685,9
Couverture des flux de trésorerie					27,9			27,9		27,9
Variations reconnues directement en capitaux propres		−			−1658,0		−370,8	−2028,8	−	−2028,8

Résultat consolidé de l'exercice				2656,0				2 656,0	1,5	2 657,5
Total des produits et charges comptabilisés			–	2656,0	–1 658,0	–	–370,8	627,2	1,5	628,7
Rémunérations payées en actions				69,1				69,1		69,1
Variation nette des titres L'Oréal autodétenus	–10486487			–1,6			–1000,0	–1001,6		–1001,6
Autres variations				9,3				9,3	–0,1	9,2
Situation au 31.12.2007	595310673	123,6	963,2	11351,8	3408,9	–1787,2	–441,1	13619,2	2,5	13621,8

TABLEAU DES FLUX DE TRÉSORERIE CONSOLIDÉS COMPARÉS

En millions d'euros

	2007	2006	2005
Flux de trésorerie liés à l'activité			
Résultat net part du groupe	2 656,0	2 061,0	1 972,3
Intérêts minoritaires	1,5	1,1	0,9
Elimination des charges et des produits sans incidence sur la trésorerie ou non liés à l'activité :			
• amortissements et provisions	598,5	579,4	426,9
• variation des impôts différés	38,3	–273,3	–290,1
• charge de rémunération des plans de stock-options (note 20.3)	69,1	49,4	29,9
• plus- ou moins-values de cessions d'actifs (note 10)	–11,7	–8,5	–11,4
• plus-value de cession Sanofi-Aventis nette d'impôt	–631,9		–
• quote-part de résultat des sociétés mises en équivalence nette des dividendes reçus	0,5	1,2	0,7
• autres opérations sans incidence sur la trésorerie	–	–	0,4
Marge brute d'autofinancement	**2 720,4**	**2 410,3**	**2 129,6**
Variation du besoin en fonds de roulement lié à l'activité (note 27)	–76,3	65,6	–35,7
Flux de trésorerie généré par l'activité (A)	**2 644,0**	**2 475,9**	**2 093,9**
Flux de trésorerie liés aux opérations d'investissement			
Acquisitions d'immobilisations corporelles et incorporelles	–776,0	–745,2	–662,3
Cessions d'immobilisations corporelles et incorporelles	30,1	28,9	11,9

Cession Sanofi-Aventis nette d'impôt	1465,3		
Variation des autres actifs financiers (y compris les titres non consolidés)	-10,2	-3,9	-37,7
Incidence des variations de périmètre (note 28)	-604,4	-1065,7	-181,7
Flux net de trésorerie lié aux opérations d'investissement (B)	**104,8**	**-1785,9**	**-869,8**
Flux de trésorerie liés aux opérations de financement			
Dividendes versés	-725,7	-633,8	-563,3
Augmentation de capital de la société mère	4,7	4,6	0,4
Valeur de cession/(acquisition) des actions autodétenues	-1001,6	-1119,0	-1193,9
Emission (remboursement) d'emprunts à court terme	-1439,1	209,3	582,0
Emission d'emprunts long terme	753,2	1563,5	100,0
Remboursement d'emprunts long terme	-10,1	-577,0	-85,0
Flux net de trésorerie lié aux opérations de financement (C)	**-2418,7**	**-552,4**	**-1159,8**
Incidence des variations de cours des devises et de juste valeur (D)	-24,6	-19,6	22,7
Variation de trésorerie (A+B+C+D)	**305,5**	**118,0**	**87,0**
Trésorerie d'ouverture (E)	**781,2**	**663,2**	**576,2**
Trésorerie de clôture (A+B+C+D+E) (note 19)	**1086,7**	**781,2**	**663,2**

Les impôts payés s'élèvent à 820,9 millions d'euros, 725,6 millions d'euros et 688,3 millions d'euros respectivement pour les exercices 2007, 2006 et 2005.
Les intérêts payés s'élèvent à 201,1 millions d'euros, 133,9 millions d'euros et 82,5 millions d'euros respectivement pour les exercices 2007, 2006 et 2005.
Les dividendes reçus s'élèvent à 250,3 millions d'euros, 217,4 millions d'euros et 171,6 millions d'euros respectivement pour les exercices 2007, 2006 et 2005.
Ceux-ci font partie de la marge brute d'autofinancement.

NOTE 4_FRAIS DE PERSONNEL ET EFFECTIFS

4.1. Effectifs [1]

	31.12.2007	31.12.2006	31.12.2005
Europe de l'Ouest	28012	27237	23903
Amérique du Nord	15107	14576	9622
Reste du monde	20239	19038	18878
Total [2]	63358	60851	52403

(1) Après prise en compte des sociétés consolidées par intégration proportionnelle.
(2) Dont 8 937 au titre de The Body Shop en 2006.

4.2. Frais de personnel

En millions d'euros	2007	2006	2005
Frais de personnel (charges sociales incluses)	3318,3	3034,9	2851,7

Les frais de personnel incluent les rémunérations liées aux stock-options ainsi que les impôts et taxes sur rémunérations.

4.3. Rémunération des dirigeants

Les charges enregistrées au titre des rémunérations et avantages assimilés accordés au Comité de Direction et au Conseil d'Administration se ventilent comme suit :

En millions d'euros	2007	2006	2005
Jetons de présence	1,0	0,9	0,9
Salaires et avantages en nature y compris charges patronales	26,3	20,2	23,4
Charges de retraite	11,2	13,1	14,5
Charges de stock-options	29,0	19,7	9,1

Le nombre des dirigeants du Comité de Direction était de 13 au 31 décembre 2007 ; il était respectivement de 9 et 10 au 31 décembre 2006 et 2005.

NOTE 5_DOTATIONS AUX AMORTISSEMENTS

Les dotations aux amortissements des immobilisations corporelles et incorporelles incluses dans les charges opérationnelles s'élèvent à 657,8, 589,5 et 541,6 millions d'euros respectivement pour 2007, 2006 et 2005.

NOTE 7_AUTRES PRODUITS ET CHARGES

Ce poste se décline comme suit :

En millions d'euros	2007	2006	2005
Plus- ou moins-values de cession d'actifs corporels et incorporels	11,8	8,5	11,5
Plus-value de cession Sanofi-Aventis (note 15)	642,8		
Dépréciation des actifs corporels et incorporels [1]	– 1,4	– 69,4	–
Coûts de restructuration [2]	– 31,6	0,1	– 2,2
Total	**621,6**	**– 60,8**	**9,3**

(1) Ces dépréciations concernent en 2006 l'écart d'acquisition de SoftSheen.Carson pour 53,7 millions d'euros ainsi que la marque Yue-Sai pour 15,7 millions d'euros.
(2) Dont 10,8 millions d'euros relatifs à l'arrêt de la distribution de Biotherm aux Etats-Unis désormais uniquement concentrée sur la promotion et la vente de ses produits sur Internet, 14 millions d'euros liés à la restructuration d'un fournisseur important de The Body Shop et 6,8 millions d'euros liés à la restructuration de la logistique en Espagne.

NOTE 22_PROVISIONS POUR RISQUES ET CHARGES

22.1. Soldes à la clôture

En millions d'euros	31.12.2007	31.12.2006	31.12.2005
Autres provisions pour risques et charges non courantes	**148,5**	**154,1**	**157,0**
Provisions pour restructuration	1,0	1,4	2,8
Autres provisions non courantes [1]	147,5	152,7	154,2
Provisions pour risques et charges courantes	**285,7**	**272,0**	**289,3**
Provisions pour restructuration	9,6	18,9	32,2
Autres provisions courantes [1]	276,1	253,1	257,1
Total	**434,2**	**426,1**	**446,3**

(1) Cette rubrique comprend notamment des provisions destinées à faire face à des risques et litiges de nature fiscale, des risques industriels et commerciaux liés à l'exploitation (ruptures de contrats, reprises de produits) et des coûts liés au personnel.

22.2. Variations de l'exercice des Provisions pour restructurations et Autres provisions pour risques et charges

En millions d'euros	31.12.2005	31.12.2006	Dotation [2]	Reprises (utilisées) [2]	Reprises (non utilisées) [2]	Incidence Périmètre/ taux de change/ Autres [1]	31.12.2007
Autres provisions pour risques et charges	411,3	405,8	183,7	–111,0	–44,1	–10,8	423,6
Provisions pour restructurations	35,0	20,3	1,6	–10,2	–0,2	–0,9	10,6
Total	**446,3**	**426,1**	**185,3**	**–121,2**	**–44,3**	**–11,7**	**434,2**

(1) Concerne pour l'essentiel des variations de change.
(2) Ces chiffres se répartissent comme suit :

NOTE 22_PROVISIONS POUR RISQUES ET CHARGES (suite)

En millions d'euros	Dotations	Reprises (utilisées)	Reprises (non utilisées)
• Autres produits et charges	1,6	−10,2	−0,2
• Résultat d'exploitation	166,4	−110,6	−40,5
• Impôts sur les résultats	17,3	−0,4	−3,6

Pour l'exercice 2006, la variation s'analysait comme suit :

En millions d'euros	31.12.2005	Dotation [2]	Reprises (utilisées) [2]	Reprises (non utilisées) [2]	Incidence Périmètre/ taux de change/ Autres [1]	31.12.2006
Autres provisions pour risques et charges	411,3	220,1	−138,9	−67,5	−19,2	405,8
Provisions pour restructurations	35,0	0,5	−13,7	−0,1	−1,4	20,3
Total	**446,3**	**220,6**	**−152,6**	**−67,6**	**−20,6**	**426,1**

(1) Concerne pour l'essentiel des variations de change.
(2) Ces chiffres se répartissent comme suit :

En millions d'euros	Dotations	Reprises (utilisées)	Reprises (non utilisées)
• Autres produits et charges	0,5	−13,7	−0,1
• Résultat d'exploitation	166,5	−134,5	−61,7
• Impôts sur les résultats	53,6	−4,4	−5,8

Pour l'exercice 2005, la variation s'analysait comme suit :

En millions d'euros	31.12.2004	Dotation [2]	Reprises (utilisées) [2]	Reprises (non utilisées) [2]	Incidence Périmètre/ taux de change/ Autres [1]	31.12.2005
Autres provisions pour risques et charges	426,9	109,8	−95,1	−60,2	29,9	411,3
Provisions pour restructurations	47,7	5,3	−15,2	−3,5	0,7	35,0
Total	**474,6**	**115,1**	**−110,3**	**−63,7**	**30,6**	**446,3**

(1) Concerne pour l'essentiel des variations de change.
(2) Ces chiffres se répartissent comme suit :

En millions d'euros	Dotations	Reprises (utilisées)	Reprises (non utilisées)
• Autres produits et charges	5,3	−15,2	−3,5
• Résultat d'exploitation	106,0	−87,2	−41,4
• Impôts sur les résultats	3,8	−7,9	−18,8

INDEX

Contents

Introduction

This series of books is intended to support the continuing growth and development of independent learning and practical activities, which are key features of the Early Years Foundation Stage (EYFS).

Children in Key Stage 1 need and deserve the chance to build on the best of practice in the EYFS, which carefully balances adult directed tasks with learning that children initiate and develop themselves, often in the company of responsive adults. These activities, which include sand and water play, construction, role play, independent mark making and writing, creative work, dance and movement, and outdoor play, are some of the activities children value most and miss most in Years 1 and 2.

What's it like in year 1?

There en't no sand and the work's too 'ard.

This quote from a Year 1 boy echoes the feelings of many children who need a continuation of the learning styles and situations offered in Reception classes. However, many teachers in Key Stage One feel intense pressure to concentrate on activities that require recording and increasing levels of direction from adults. Why is this, and is it right for teachers to feel so pressured?

One thing we know from research is that practical activity and independent learning are essential for brain growth and reinforcement of growing abilities throughout childhood, at least until the onset of puberty, and for many children this is a lifelong need. We also know that the embedding of learning and the transformation of this into real understanding takes time and practice. Skills need to be reinforced by revisiting them in many different contexts in child-initiated learning and practical

challenges. Practical tasks in real life situations will be far more effective than rote learning, worksheets or adult direction.

It is also clear from brain research that many boys (and some girls) are just not ready by the end of Reception to embark on a formal curriculum which involves a lot of sitting down, listening and writing. Their bodies and their brains still need action, challenge and freedom to explore materials and resources.

But this does not mean that challenge should be absent from such activity! The brain feeds on challenge and novelty, so teachers and other adults working in Key Stage One need to structure the experiences, so they build on existing skills and previous activities, while presenting opportunities to explore familiar materials in new and exciting ways. Such challenges and activities can:

- be led by the Programme of Study for Key Stage 1
- focus on thinking skills and personal capabilities
- relate to real world situations and stimuli
- help children to achieve the five outcomes for Every Child Matters.

'I hear and I forget,
I see and I remember,
I do and I understand.'
Ancient Chinese Proverb

Every Child Matters

The five outcomes:

- Enjoy and achieve
- Stay safe
- Be healthy
- Make a positive contribution
- Achieve economic well-being

Carrying on in Key Stage 1

Outdoor Play

Published 2011 by A&C Black Publishers Limited
36 Soho Square, London W1D 3QY

www.acblack.com

ISBN 978-1-4081-3978-3

First published 2008 by Featherstone Education Ltd

Text © Ros Bayley, Lyn Broadbent, Sally Featherstone 2008

Photographs © Fotolia 2011, Shutterstock 2011

Additional photos © Lynn Broadbent, Ros Bayley, Sally Featherstone, Sarah Featherstone 2008, ASCO

Designed by Lynda Murray

A CIP record for this publication is available from the British Library.

Printed in Malta by Gutenburg Press Ltd

This book is produced using paper that is made from wood grown in managed, sustainable forests. It is natural, renewable and recyclable.

The logging and manufacturing processes conform to the environmental regulations of the country of origin.

To see our full range of titles visit **www.acblack.com**

In **Carrying on in Key Stage 1**, we aim to give you the rationale, the process and the confidence to continue a practical, child-centred curriculum which also helps you as teachers to meet the requirements of the statutory curriculum for Key Stage One. Each book in the series follows the same format, and addresses objectives from many areas of the National Curriculum. Of course, when children work on practical challenges, curriculum elements become intertwined, and many will be going on simultaneously.

The role of the adult

Of course, even during child-initiated learning, the role of the adult is crucial. Sensitive adults play many roles as they support, challenge and engage the children in their care. High quality teaching is not easy! If teachers want to expand experiences and enhance learning, they need to be able to stand back, to work alongside, and to extend or scaffold the children's learning by offering provocations and challenges to their thinking. The diagram on the right attempts to describe this complex task, and the way that adults move around the elements in the circle of learning. For ease of reading we have described the elements in the following way, and each double page spread covers all three of the vital roles adults play.

Previous experience: recognising and building on the practical activities which children have experienced before

This element of the process is vital in scaffolding children's learning so it makes sense to them. Your knowledge of the Foundation Stage curriculum and the way it is organised will be vital in knowing where to start.
Teachers and other adults should have first hand knowledge of both the resources and the activities which have been available and how they have been offered in both child-initiated and adult-led activities. This knowledge should be gained by visiting the Reception classes in action, and by talking to adults and children as they work. Looking at Reception planning will also help.

The responsive adult: Understanding the range of adult roles, and the effect different roles have on children's learning

Responsive adults react in different ways to what they see and hear during the day. This knowledge will influence the way they plan for further experiences to meet emerging needs and build on individual interests. The diagram illustrates the complex and interlinking ways in which adults interact with children's learning. Observing, co-playing and extending learning often happen simultaneously, flexibly and sometimes unconsciously. It is only when we reflect on our work with children that we realise what a complex and skilled activity is going on.

Offering challenges and provocations

As the adults collect information about the learning, they begin to see how they can help children to extend and scaffold their thinking and learning. The adults offer challenges or provocations which act like grit in an oyster, provoking the children to produce responses and think in new ways about what they know and can do.

Linking the learning with the skills and content of the curriculum

As the children grapple with new concepts and skills, adults can make direct links with curriculum intentions and content. These links can be mapped out across the range of knowledge, skills and understanding contained in the curriculum guidance for Key Stage One. It is also possible to map the development of thinking skills, personal capabilities and concepts which link the taught curriculum with the real world.

The adult as extender of learning
- discusses ideas
- shares thinking
- makes new possibilities evident
- instigates new opportunities for learning
- extends and builds on learning and interests
- supports children in making links in learning
- models new skills and techniques

The adult as co-player
- shares responsibility with the child
- offers suggestions
- asks open questions
- responds sensitively
- models and imitates
- plays alongside

The adult as observer
- listens attentively
- observes carefully
- records professionally
- interprets skilfully

Looking for the learning

Assessment for learning involves adults and children in sharing and analysing what they discover. Reflecting on learning, through discussion with other children and adults, is a key factor in securing skills and abilities, fixing and 'hard wiring' the learning in each child's brain. And, of course, teachers and other adults need to recognise, confirm and record children's achievements, both for the self esteem this brings to the children and to fulfil their own duties as educators.

You could find out what children already know and have experienced by:

- talking to them as individuals and in small groups

- talking to parents and other adults who know them well (teaching assistants are often wonderful sources of information about individual children)

- visiting the Reception classes and looking at spaces, storage and access to resources, including the use of these out of doors

- providing free access to materials and equipment and watching how children use them when you are not giving any guidance

- talking as a group or class about what children already know about the materials and those they particularly enjoy using.

Using the curriculum grid to observe, to recognise learning and celebrate achievement

At the end of this section you will find a photocopiable curriculum grid covering the whole Programme of Study for Key Stage 1 which can be used for planning and particularly for recording observations. This is a 'shorthand version' of the full grid included at the end of the book on pages 40-48.

We suggest that as the children work on the provocations and other challenges in this book, adults (teachers and teaching assistants) can use the grid to observe groups of children and record the areas of the curriculum they are covering in their work. The grid can also be used to record what children say and describe in plenary sessions and other discussions.

These observations will enable you to recognise the learning that happens as children explore the materials and engage with the challenging questions you ask and the problems you pose. And of course, as you observe, you will begin to see what needs to happen next; identifying the next steps in learning! This logical and vital stage in the process may identify:

- some children who will be ready for more of the same activity

- some who need to repeat and reinforce previous stages

- some who need to relate skills to new contexts, the same activity or skill practised in a new place or situation

- some who will want to extend or sustain the current activity in time, space or detail

- others who will wish to record their work in photos, drawings, models, stories, video and so on.

The grid also identifies the key skills which children need for thinking about and evaluating their work. Many schools now observe and evaluate how well these skills are developing when children work on challenging projects and investigations.

Ready for more?

Offering extension activities is a way of scaffolding children's learning, taking the known into the unknown, the familiar into the new, the secure into the challenging. It is the role of the adult to turn their knowledge of the children into worthwhile, long-term lines of enquiry and development which will become self-sustaining and last throughout life.

At the end of each section in the book you will find a selection of useful resources, links and other information to help you support children in making structures, sculptures and other 3D creations. You could use these resources by encouraging individuals and groups:

- to use the Internet to find images and information

- to use ICT equipment such as cameras, tape recorders, video and dictaphones to record their explorations and experiments

- to explore information books in libraries and other places at home and at school

- to make contact by email and letter with experts, craftsmen, artists, manufacturers, suppliers and other contacts

- to make books, films, PowerPoint presentations

- to record their work in photographs and other media

- to respond to stimuli such as photographs, video, exhibitions and other creative stimuli

- to look at the built and natural environment with curiosity, interest and creativity

- to become involved in preserving the natural world, develop environmental awareness and support recycling

- to look at the world of work and extend their ideas of what they might become and how they might live their lives

- to develop a sense of economic awareness and the world of work in its widest sense

- to feel a sense of community and to explore how they might make a contribution to the school and wider communities in which they live

- to work together and develop the ability to think, reason and solve problems in their learning.

The suggested resources include websites, books, contacts and addresses. There are also some photographs which may inspire young learners as they work on the provocations and challenges suggested.

We hope you will find the ideas in this book useful in stimulating your work with children in Year 1 and Year 2. Before trying the activities please check for allergies and be aware of safety at all times. The ideas, photos and provocations we have included are only a start to your thinking and exploring together. Of course you and the children will have many more as you start to expand the work they do in these practical areas, providing a rich curriculum base using familiar and well loved materiaals.

We recommend that younger children should always work with an adult when accessing search engines and Internet sites.

Planning and observation of _____ (the activity)

Literacy

Lit 1 Speak	Lit 2 Listen	Lit 3 Group	Lit 4 Drama	Lit 5 Word	Lit 6 Spell	Lit 7 Text 1	Lit 8 Text 2	Lit 9 Text 3	Lit 10 Text 4	Lit 11 Sentence	Lit 12 Presentation
1.1	2.1	3.1	4.1	5.1	6.1	7.1	8.1	9.1	10.1	11.1	12.1
1.2	2.2	3.2	4.2	5.2	6.2	7.2	8.2	9.2	10.2	11.2	12.2

Numeracy

Num 1 U&A	Num 2 Count	Num 3 Number	Num 4 Calculate	Num 5 Shape	Num 6 Measure	Num 7 Data
1.1	2.1	3.1	4.1	5.1	6.1	7.1
1.2	2.2	3.2	4.2	5.2	6.2	7.2

Name	Date

Science

SC1 Enquiry			SC2 Life processes					SC3 Materials		SC4 Physical processes		
Sc 1.1	Sc 1.2	Sc 1.3	Sc 2.1	Sc 2.2	Sc 2.3	Sc 2.4	Sc 2.5	Sc 3.1	Sc 3.2	Sc 4.1	Sc4.2	Sc 4.3
1.1a	1.2a	1.3a	2.1a	2.2a	2.3a	2.4a	2,5a	3.1a	3.2a	4.1a	4.2a	4.3a
1.1b	1.2b	1.3b	2.1b	2.2b	2.3b	2.4b	2,5b	3.1b	3.2b	4.1b	4.2b	4.3b
1.1c	1.2c	1.3c	2.1c	2.2c	2.3c		2,5c	3.1c		4.1c	4.2c	4.3c
1.1d				2.2d				3.1d				4.3d
				2.2e								
				2.2f								
				2.2g								

History

H1 Chronology	H2 Events, people	H3 Interpret	H4 Enquire	H5 Org and comm	H6 Breadth
1a	2a	3a	4a	5a	6a
1b	2b		4b		6b
				6c	
				6d	

Geography

G1.1and G1.2 Enquiry		G2 Places	G3 Processes	G4 Environment	G5 Breadth
1.1a	1.2a	2a	3a	4a	5a
1.1b	1.2b	2b	3b	4b	5b
1.1c	1.2c	2c			5c
1.1d	1.2d	2d			5d
		2e			

Notes on how to take the learning forward

Music

M1 Performing	M2 Composing	M3 Appraising	M4 Listening	M5 Breadth
1a	2a	3a	4a	5a
1b	2b	3b	4b	5b
1c			4c	5c
			5d	

Art and Design

A&D 1 Ideas	A&D 2 Making	A&D 3 Evaluating	A&D 4 Materials	A&D 5 Breadth
1a	2a	3a	4a	5a
1b	2b	3b	4b	5b
	2c		4c	5c
				5d

Design and Technology

D&T 1 Developing	D&T 2 Tool use	D&T 3 Evaluating	D&T 4 Materials	D&T 5 Breadth
1a	2a	3a	4a	5a
1b	2b	3b	4b	5b
1c	2c			5c
1d	2d			
1e	2e			

PSHE

PSHE1 Confidence and respect	PSHE2 Citizenship	PSHE3 Health	PSHE4 Relationships
1a	2a	3a	4a
1b	2b	3b	4b
1c	2c	3c	4c
1d	2d	3d	4d
1e	2e	3e	4e
	2f	3f	
	2g	3g	
	2h		

ICT

ICT 1 Finding out		ICT2 Ideas	ICT3 Reviewing	ICT4 Breadth
1.1a	1.2a	2a	3a	4a
1.1b	1.2b	2b	3b	4b
1.1c	1.2c	2c	3c	4c
	1.2d			

PE

PE 1 Develop skills	PE 2 Apply skills	PE 3 Evaluate	PE 4 Fitness	PE 5 Breadth
1a	2a	3a	4a	5a dance
1b	2b	3b	4b	5b games
	2c	3c		5c gym

Critical skills	Thinking skills
problem solving	observing
decision making	classifying
critical thinking	prediction
creative thinking	making inferences
communication	problem solving
organisation	drawing conclusions
management	
leadership	

Tyres, ropes and pulleys

Previous experience

Most children will have had experience of using these sorts of resources, and some will have had free access to them for building their own structures and experimenting with these materials in:

- free play, constructing, lifting, tying and pulling
- rolling tyres, building towers
- tying pulleys and ropes to climbing frames and other fixed apparatus
- lifting buckets and baskets, full or empty
- attaching to wheeled vehicles for pulling and fixing
- games involving jumping on, in and over tyres and ropes
- making shelters and dens with ropes, fabrics and other construction materials.

The responsive adult

In the early stages of working with these materials it is crucial to continue to observe the children. Only by doing this can you set developmentally appropriate challenges and provocations. The ideas listed here are offered as suggestions; the most exciting challenges will arise from children's own interests and motivations, which will only become apparent as you spend time with them, watching and joining them in their play. As you do this, you will be moving between the three interconnecting roles of observer, co-player, extender described below, and will be able to decide what you need to do next to take the learning forward. In three interconnecting roles, the responsive adult will be:

Observer

- observing
- listening
- interpreting

Co-player

- modelling
- playing alongside
- offering suggestions
- responding sensitively
- initiating with care!

Extender

- discussing ideas
- sharing thinking
- modelling new skills
- asking open questions
- being an informed extender
- instigating ideas and thoughts
- supporting children as they make links in learning
- making possibilities evident
- introducing new ideas and resources
- offering challenges and provocations

Offering challenges and provocations

As children get older they can use ropes, pulleys and tyres in conjunction with other flexible resources to experiment with materials, structures and forces. They may need some support at the start, if these resources are not familiar to them, but once they are used to flexible materials they will be able to respond to all sorts of scientific and technological challenges.

- Can you use tyres to support a waterway?

- How can you use a pulley to lift a basket higher than your head? How can you fix the rope so the basket stays up?

- Look at some pictures of flagpoles, or a real one if you know where to find one. How do flagpoles work and how does the flag go up and down on the rope?

- Use a piece of fabric to make a flag. Paint a design on it and find a place where you could fly the flag. Use thin rope to make a pulley, so you can raise and lower your flag when you need to.

- Make some bunting for your outdoor area. Bunting is lots of little flags in a row. Hang it on a rope with a pulley.

- Look at some tyres on Google. How many different sorts can you find? Now find some tyres in the Lego set or toy car tyres. How do tyres work? What are they made from?

- Use the toy tyres to make a painting by rolling them in paint and then using them to print on paper.

- Now try spreading some paint or mud on a flat surface outside and using the tyres to make tracks. Photograph the different tracks. Try the same thing with some real tyres.

- Use the tyres in your outdoor area to build a tower — how high can you build it? Can you make the tyres into a tunnel?

- Make up a game with tyres and ropes, where you have to jump, go through, over and under. Use chalk to make markings if you need them. Then invite your friends to play the game and see who is best at it.

Ready for more?

- Find out about prayer flags by putting 'prayer flags' in Google images. Can you make some prayer flags for your outdoor area? Decorate them with pictures, patterns or words.

- Find some pulleys and rope. Can you make a pulley system that will lift a weight that you can't easily lift yourself? Putting the heavy things in a bucket or container with a handle will help. Take some photos of your experiments.

- Use a colander or sieve, and find a way to suspend it above a bucket or water tray (look at the pictures here). Can you raise and lower the colander by using a simple pulley?

- If you can get a bike to look at, investigate how the cogs in bike chains work. Draw a diagram of the chain and cogs of a bike and label all the parts. Now describe how it works.

- Find out about the sorts of pulleys used by sailors, firemen, farmers, vets and Air Sea Rescue helicopters. You can look in books or on the internet. Make a book of your findings.

- Use tyres to make these things:
  - a flower planter
  - a sand pit
  - a pond that holds water
  - a bog garden.

Take photos of your inventions.

Materials, websites, books and other references

Materials

For simple pulleys, use:

- cotton reels or bobbins to wind string or rope round;
- short lengths of hard plastic tubing;
- pieces from construction sets such as Lego, Gears or Connect
- the hubs from toy cars, with the tyres removed.

For pulleys with ropes try:

www.tts-group.co.uk

www.mindstretchers

www.ascoeducational.co.uk

www.eduzone.co.uk

Contact any tyre fitting business and they will probably be delighted to give you some tyres. They may even deliver them to you! Some tyres leave a black residue on hands and clothing, so check the ones you use.

Google images

- tyre
- pulley
- flagpole

Websites

www.ise5-14.org.uk/Prim3/New_guidelines/Newsletters (newsletter & challenges)

automata.co.uk/pulleys - for moving figures

www.ehow.com/how_1277_make-simple-pulley - activity

www.mikids.com/Smachines - pulleys

www.sciencetech.technomuses.ca/english/schoolzone/activities (pulley activity sheet)

www.42explore.com/smplmac - links to lots of websites for simple mechanics

outreach.rice.edu - teacher materials

www.dorsetforyou.com/media/pdf/r/b/Pre_school_outdoor_environment.pdf - for a downloadable booklet on outdoor play with a section on tyres

www.ehow.com/how_1276_build-block-tackle

www.athropolis.com/links/how-work - how lots of things work

Books

Pulleys (Simple Machines); Michael Dahl; Franklin Watts Ltd

Levers (Simple Machines); Michael Dahl; Franklin Watts Ltd

Levers Big Book (Very Useful Machines); Chris Oxlade; Heinemann

Pulleys (Very Useful Machines); Chris Oxlade; Heinemann Library

Ramps and Wedges (Very Useful Machines); Chris Oxlade; Heinemann Library

Amazing Machines (Design Challenge); Keith Good; Evans Brothers Ltd

Play Equipment for Kids; Great Projects You Can Build; Storey Books, US

Boxes and cartons

Previous experience

Empty cardboard boxes are a free resource for all schools and now a feature of most early years settings. The majority of children will have experimented with and explored these resources in:

- building and stacking
- assembling and dis-assembling
- to make homes and habitats for toys, vehicles and puppets
- building small worlds
- making dens
- cutting boxes up to make other things
- fitting boxes inside each other
- making parcels and presents.

The responsive adult

In the early stages of working with these materials it is crucial to continue to observe the children. Only by doing this can you set developmentally appropriate challenges and provocations. The ideas listed here are offered as suggestions; the most exciting challenges will arise from children's own interests and motivations, which will only become apparent as you spend time with them, watching and joining them in their play. As you do this, you will be moving between the three interconnecting roles of observer, co-player, extender described below, and will be able to decide what you need to do next to take the learning forward. In three interconnecting roles, the responsive adult will be:

Observer

- observing
- listening
- interpreting

Co-player

- modelling
- playing alongside
- offering suggestions
- responding sensitively
- initiating with care!

Extender

- discussing ideas
- sharing thinking
- modelling new skills
- asking open questions
- being an informed extender
- instigating ideas and thoughts
- supporting children as they make links in learning
- making possibilities evident
- introducing new ideas and resources
- offering challenges and provocations

Offering challenges and provocations

- Can you use boxes to create:
  - a home for a soft toy?
  - a garage for a car or truck?
  - a home for a small world character?
- Can you join cardboard boxes together to make a tunnel? Is it big enough for you to crawl through?
- What is the longest tunnel you can make?
- Can you create a tunnel that goes round corners?
- Can you fix cartons or boxes together to make a tower taller than you? Now find three different ways to measure your tower.
- Can you use boxes and cartons to make:
  - a suit of armour?
  - a hobby horse?
  - a space-suit?
  - a robot?
  - a windmill?
  - a Chinese dragon?

- Find some corrugated cardboard. How can you use this to make printed patterns?
- Can you make a notice board from the card from boxes? Make your notice board attractive, and find a way to hang it up, indoors or outside.
- Can you use big cardboard boxes to make a den for yourself and your friends? Put 'building dens' into Google to get some ideas.
- Cut a very big box up to make a puppet theatre, find some puppets and then make up a puppet show for your friends.
- Make a TV set that you can put over your head. Now can you be a weather presenter or a comedian?
- What can you use to waterproof a cardboard box? Try some of your ideas.

Ready for more?

- Can you use boxes to make a den with more than one room? Then can you make your den fold up so you can store it?

- Can you find a way to paint or wallpaper the inside of your den? What is the best material to use?

- Google 'cardboard classroom' or 'westborough school' to find a school classroom that really is made from cardboard. How do you think they made it?

- Can you make some windows and a door in your house?

- Put 'cardboard furniture' in Google and find some designs and ideas for making your own. Then put **www.paperpod.co.uk** in a search and see what you can find. You could send for a catalogue or try to make a cardboard chair or rocket yourselves.

- Cut some shapes from the cardboard and add things to them to make a mobile for your classroom. Can you make it waterproof so it can hang outside? Can you make a musical mobile by adding things to the cardboard?

- Find some strong boxes and make a drum kit. What will you use for drumsticks?

- Can you turn a box into a weaving loom? What do you need to add? Does it work?

- Can you use the cardboard from a carton to make a small gift box or a habitat for a small creature?

Materials

You can get boxes, cartons and tyres from:

- supermarkets or shops that sell white goods such as washing machines. Carpet shops will often give tubes from carpet rolls.

- tyre service centres such as Kwik-Fit will be glad to get rid of tyres, and some may have tractor and digger tyres too.

- builders' trays (or cement mixing trays) are very useful for containing the water during experiments. Get these from DIY superstores such as B&Q, Wilkinson's or Homebase.

- bargain or 'Pound' shops are good sources for plastic crates, boxes and bowls of all sizes and shapes.

- supermarkets and diaries will specialise in vegetable, drink and milk bottle crates.

Websites

www.make-stuff.com/kids has some great projects including a cardboard castle.

www.terragenesis.co.uk model castle using textured paint.

www.360models.co.uk is an architectural model site - look at their gallery of models for ideas.

www.ecocentric.co.uk sell a model castle and other toys made from recycled cardboard.

Google images

Try typing in:

- cardboard box

- chair cardboard box

- rocket cardboard box

- cardboard box house/castle.

Books

Some suitable fiction books for younger readers include:

My Cat Likes to Hide in Boxes; Eve Sutton; Puffin Books

Not a Box; Antoinette Portis; HarperCollins Children's Books

The Shoe Box; Francine Rivers; Tyndale House Publishers

Jack in a Box; Julia Jarman; HarperCollins Children's Books

Non Fiction:

The Little Book of Bricks and Boxes; Clare Beswick; A & C Black

Creative Crafts from Cardboard Boxes; Nikki Conner; Copper Beech Books

The Cardboard Box Book; Watson-Guptill Publications

Egg Carton Mania; Christine M. Irvin; Children's Press

Likable Recyclables; Linda Schwartz; Learning Works

Make It with Cardboard; Anna Olimos Plomer; Book House

The Big Box; Toni Morrison; Saint Martin's Press Inc.

Bricks and blocks

Previous experience

By the time children leave the Foundation Stage they should have had wide experience of using bricks and blocks of all sorts and sizes:

- in free play indoors and out of doors;
- to make structures and buildings;
- in play with small world animals and figures;
- to explore balance, stability and form;
- for towers and fantasy landscapes;
- to make child-sized walls, shelters and dens.

They should also have had experience of:

- working on specific projects with bricks, such as making houses for story characters or habitats for creatures;
- experimenting with non-standard units such as sawn logs; and with real bricks.

The responsive adult

In the early stages of working with these materials it is crucial to continue to observe the children. Only by doing this can you set developmentally appropriate challenges and provocations. The ideas listed here are offered as suggestions; the most exciting challenges will arise from children's own interests and motivations, which will only become apparent as you spend time with them, watching and joining them in their play. As you do this, you will be moving between the three interconnecting roles of observer, co-player, extender described below, and will be able to decide what you need to do next to take the learning forward. In three interconnecting roles, the responsive adult will be:

Observer

- observing
- listening
- interpreting

Co-player

- modelling
- playing alongside
- offering suggestions
- responding sensitively
- initiating with care!

Extender

- discussing ideas
- sharing thinking
- modelling new skills
- asking open questions
- being an informed extender
- instigating ideas and thoughts
- supporting children as they make links in learning
- making possibilities evident
- introducing new ideas and resources
- offering challenges and provocations

Offering challenges and provocations

It is important to find out the breadth of experience children have had during the Foundation Stage, particularly in using bricks out of doors. You may also want to dicuss non-standard and real brick units with them exploring the challenges of working with these, before embarking on independent challenges and provocations.

- Get a set of wooden bricks. How many different ways can you sort them before using them to build with? Make a chart or take photos to show what you did.

- Can you build a habitat for minibeasts out of doors with bricks or sawn branches? Leave the habitat out for several days and see if any minibeasts move in.

- Try making several different habitats in different places outside. You could add bark, twigs, leaves and other natural materials to the bricks. Take photos of all the habitats and see what happens to them over time.

- Can you make an enclosed structure with wooden bricks? What can you use for a roof?

- Use bricks and guttering to make a water-way or sandway that goes at least two metres. What is the best way of using the bricks?

- Use real bricks with planks to make a roadway for toy cars. What is the longest roadway you can make? Can you make it in a way that cars will run all the way along it without needing you to push them?

- Can you prop up a drainpipe or cardboard tube with bricks so cars can race down it? Mark where the cars finish and experiment with making a run that propels cars the furthest. Record your results.

- Can you make a structure with bricks that is big enough to get inside?

Materials, websites, books and other references

Materials

Educational suppliers all have a range of wooden and plastic bricks of various sizes - try www.tts-group.co.uk, www.ascoeducational.co.uk or your local consortium group.

The best wooden bricks are from Community Playthings www.communityplaythings.co.uk - they are expensive but very hardwearing, precision cut and great to build with. Download a free leaflet on brick building from this site too.

Make your own sets of building blocks from sawn branches (look for some after a storm and saw them into suitable lengths (the children could do this!). Or contact your local Parks Department to see if they can help. They may be able to give you some slices of tree trunks, which give children a real challenge.

Local colleges may have bricklaying courses and students may be able to visit you, and of course, you could ask parents and relatives to come and demonstrate their skills.

Ready for more?

◆ Go outside and look at some walls. Record what you see with a camera. How are brick walls built so they don't fall down? Experiment with making walls with wooden bricks that look like real brick walls.

◆ Now try the above experiment with real bricks. You might be able to use some real cement to fix them together.

◆ Find some bricks and planks, and experiment with making bridges. What is the longest bridge you can make? How can you prop up the spans? Take photos of your experiments.

◆ Look at bridges on the internet. What is the longest bridge in the world? Download some pictures from Google or internet sites and use these with your bridge photos to make a book or display. If you laminate the pictures, you could make an outdoor book or display.

◆ Work with some friends. Use all the bricks and blocks you can find to make a huge construction out of doors. Take as long as you need. Your construction could be a city, a space port, a castle, an airport or any other construction. You could work big, high or wide. Take some photos as you work. Add small world people, animals and vehicles. Make signs and notices. Use chalk or paint if you need it. Invent a name for your construction.

Websites

www.diydoctor.org.uk/projects/laybricksandblocks has a sheet on block building with real bricks.

www.buildingcentre.co.uk is the centre for the building industry.

Google images

- bricks
- brick building
- wooden bricks
- brick castle
- children building.

Books

Some suitable books for younger readers include:

A Day with a Brick Layer; Mark Thomas; Children's Press

Building Tools; Inez Snyder; Children's Press

Building Bridges; David Glover; Longman

Castles; A 3-Dimensional Exploration; Gillian Osband; Tango Books

What Were Castles For?; Phil Roxbee Cox; Usborne Publishing Ltd

A Picture History of Great Buildings; Gillian Clements; Frances Lincoln

Bridge Building; Diana Briscoe; Red Brick Learning

A City Through Time; Philip Steele; DK Publishing

Atlantis: The Legend of a Lost City; Christina Balit; Frances Lincoln

Habitats; Where Wildlife Lives; Sally Hewitt; Franklin Watts Ltd

All Kinds of Habitats; Sally Hewitt; Franklin Watts Ltd

The Great Outdoors; Saving Habitats (You Can Save the Planet); Richard Spilsbury; Heinemann

Sound and music

Previous experience

During their time in the Foundation Stage, children will have explored both home made and commercially produced instruments in a wide range of contexts:

- in free play indoors and out of doors
- to explore and discriminate between sounds
- to accompany songs and jingles
- when playing listening games
- to produce sound effects to accompany traditional tales and stories, and to make sound pictures
- to make music for dances
- to play along with recorded music.

They should also have listened to a wide range of music from a variety of cultures.

The responsive adult

In the early stages of working with these materials it is crucial to continue to observe the children. Only by doing this can you set developmentally appropriate challenges and provocations. The ideas listed here are offered as suggestions; the most exciting challenges will arise from children's own interests and motivations, which will only become apparent as you spend time with them, watching and joining them in their play. As you do this, you will be moving between the three interconnecting roles of observer, co-player, extender described below, and will be able to decide what you need to do next to take the learning forward. In three interconnecting roles, the responsive adult will be:

Observer

- observing
- listening
- interpreting

Co-player

- modelling
- playing alongside
- offering suggestions
- responding sensitively
- initiating with care!

Extender

- discussing ideas
- sharing thinking
- modelling new skills
- asking open questions
- being an informed extender
- instigating ideas and thoughts
- supporting children as they make links in learning
- making possibilities evident
- introducing new ideas and resources
- offering challenges and provocations

Offering challenges and provocations

When setting up a music area, try to make it near a dressing up/performance area so these elements of play can be incorporated. A simple CD player is another piece of equipment worth considering.

- Can you design and make an outside music area using found and recycled materials? Look on the Internet for 'Bash the Trash' for ideas. (Other ideas opposite).

- How many different kinds of shakers can you make, using:
  - paper or plastic cups
  - tins with lids
  - bowls and buckets
  - plastic bottles
  - bottle tops?

  Fill them with all sorts of small objects. Which works best? Which makes the best sound? Which is loudest, which is softest?

- Use your shakers to accompany music on a CD or some songs. Can you keep a beat with your shaker?

- Can you make some music with these things:
  - saucepans
  - saucepan lids
  - old cutlery
  - chains
  - plastic bottles
  - bottle tops or ring pulls?

- Design and make some instruments for a marching band. Plan your route. Practise some good rhythms that are easy to march to. Have a parade.

- Find some drumsticks or chopsticks, and use these to explore the sounds you can make outside. Which things make the highest sounds, which make the lowest sounds? Can you play a tune?

Ready for more?

♦ Create sound stories on these themes:

 • a walk in the woods

 • a stormy day

 • a walk on the beach

 • a visit to the zoo

 • a volcano erupting

 • superheroes rescuing someone.

♦ Choose some of your favourite story books and make up sound effects to accompany the story.

♦ Make your own drum kit or percussion set from recycled materials.

♦ Can you use musical instruments to send messages? Work with friends to make a secret message system.

♦ Research on the internet and in books to find out everything you can about:

 • carnivals

 • circuses

 • festivals

 • talent shows.

♦ Plan your own show or event.

♦ Make up some sound games, by recording sounds out of doors and seeing if your friends can guess what they are. Try the games with the children in reception or the nursery.

♦ Write and perform a sound track for a puppet show or a play you have made up with friends.

♦ Find some ways of writing down your music, so other people can play it too.

Materials

Musical instruments are much more fun out of doors, because the sounds carry further and there is not a limit on noise! You can provide a simple trolley with instruments, fabrics, ribbon sticks and other movement equipment for free expression of specific tasks and challenges. Encourage children to make their own sound makers and instruments as well, from recycled and simple materials.

The following sites give guidance on providing more permanent musical experiences out of doors, as well as tips on providing simple, inexpensive features to extend creativity through music and dance:

Websites

www.bingbangbong.info for musical instruments

www.mindstretchers.co.uk more instruments to use out of doors

www.butlersheetmetal.com make your own steel drum

www.mudcat.org/kids/drums for simple home-made drums

www.artistshelpingchildren.org has a page on making your own musical instruments

www.4to40.com has instructions for a mini-dustbin drum

www.worcestershire.gov.uk where you can download a free leaflet on outdoor music

www.freenotes.net an American firm that installs outdoor musical equipment - good picture gallery

www.education-show.com has information about outdoor music suppliers

Materials, websites, books and other references

Books

The Little Book of Junk Music; Simon MacDonald; A & C Black

101 Music Games for Children; G. Storms; Hunter House

Game-songs with Prof. Dogg's Troupe; Harriet Powell; A & C Black

The Happy Hedgehog Band; Martin Waddell; Barefoot Books

The Singing Sack: 28 Song-stories from Around the World; Helen East; A&C Black

Doing the Animal Bop (with CD); Lindsey Gardiner; Barron's Educational Series

The Big Book of Music Games; Debra Olsen Pressnall; Instructional Fair

High Low Dolly Pepper: Developing Basic Music Skills with Young Children; Veronica Clark; A&C Black

Dance and movement

Previous experience

Moving and dancing are part of the Early Years Foundation Stage curriculum. Children will probably have danced in free play as well as in adult led sessions. They will have responded to a range of stimuli such as:

- drapes, net and ribbons
- scarves
- elastic and lycra
- balls, hoops and beanbags.

Their dances may have evolved around:

- stories and poems
- pictures and photographs
- seasonal themes
- themes from nature
- artefacts;

and been inspired by music from a wide range of cultures.

The responsive adult

In the early stages of working with these materials it is crucial to continue to observe the children. Only by doing this can you set developmentally appropriate challenges and provocations. The ideas listed here are offered as suggestions; the most exciting challenges will arise from children's own interests and motivations, which will only become apparent as you spend time with them, watching and joining them in their play. As you do this, you will be moving between the three interconnecting roles of observer, co-player, extender described below, and will be able to decide what you need to do next to take the learning forward. In three interconnecting roles, the responsive adult will be:

Observer

- observing
- listening
- interpreting

Co-player

- modelling
- playing alongside
- offering suggestions
- responding sensitively
- initiating with care!

Extender

- discussing ideas
- sharing thinking
- modelling new skills
- asking open questions
- being an informed extender
- instigating ideas and thoughts
- supporting children as they make links in learning
- making possibilities evident
- introducing new ideas and resources
- offering challenges and provocations

Offering challenges and provocations

In most cases, if children are to be involved in choreographing their own dances, they will first need experience of the process in adult modelled and adult supported sessions. Once this has happened, as long as they have access to the materials they need, and time to get involved, children will practise and extend what they have learned.

- Make dances linked to popular stories:
  - *Where the Wild Things are*
  - *Funny Bones*
  - *The Hungry Caterpillar*
  - *Rainbow Fish*.
- Create dances with ribbons and streamers, exploring different pathways and levels:
  - zig-zags
  - curved lines and swooping arcs
  - straight lines and sharp turns
  - high and low levels
  - backwards and forwards.
- How might the dance look different if you use drapes, scarves or 'cheerleader pompoms'?

- Find out all you can about these sorts of dancing:
  - Bangra dancing
  - line dancing
  - square dancing
  - maypole dancing
  - barn dancing
  - Scottish or Irish dancing
  - Greek dancing and Flamenco
  - African, Australian and other national dances.
    - Can you do these dances - Jive, Rock and Roll, Limbo, Salsa, ballroom, or find out how to do them? You could ask your parents and grandparents to show you, and then have a show!

Ready for more?

♦ Can you devise a dance for:

- two people?

- three people?

- four people?

- more than ten people?

♦ Get some lycra and sew it into cylinders. Get inside and see how many different shapes you can make as you move your body. Can you fit more than one person inside to make a better shape?

♦ Get a friend to take some photos of you as you make shapes in the lycra tube.

♦ Collect some movement words by looking in word books or on the internet. How many different ones can you find? Make a list and pin it up so you can add more when you find them.

♦ Choose six of your words and join the movements together to make a movement sentence.

♦ Now make up lots more movement sentences. If you work in a group, you could have a narrator who says the words as you move.

♦ Make a performance area outside, and plan your own dance festival. Make invitations, tickets and programmes. Make up some dances, and invite some people to come and see your festival.

♦ Look on the internet and in books for some movement games. Try some of these out. Make a collection or scrapbook of games for your class to play.

Materials, websites, books and other references

Materials

Try www.spacekraft.co.uk for ribbon sticks, 'body sox' lycra suits, latex tube band for group work, or make your own using lengths of ribbon from markets and florists, tied to green garden sticks, chopsticks or even pencils.

Make cheer leader pompoms from fabric or thin carrier bags, cut in strips and tied in the middle to make a ball. Look at www.sport-thieme.co.uk to see examples.

www.novelties-direct.co.uk - has a great selection of pompoms at reasonable prices.

Websites

www.cheerleading.org.uk/schools - the UK cheerleader website - where you can download a free leaflet on starting cheerleading in your school!

www.teachingideas.co.uk/music - gives some ideas for simple rhythm activities.

www.nncc.org has more information on rhythm.

www.standards.dfes.gov.uk/pdf/primaryschemes - has the QCA scheme of work for a unit of work for Years 1/2 on 'feel the Pulse - Exploring Pulse and Rhythm'

Google Images

For images of dance and dancers, try:

- children dancing

- ribbon sticks

- cheerleader

- cheerleader pompoms.

Books

Some suitable books to use with younger children include:

Let's Go, Zudie-o: Creative Activities for Dance and Music (Book and CD); Helen MacGregor; A & C Black

Helping Young children with Steady Beat; Ros Bayley, Lynn Broadbent; Lawrence Educational

Steady Beat Songs; Ros Bayley; Lawrence Educational

101 Dance Games for Children: Fun & Creativity with Movement; Paul Rooyackers; Hunter House

101 More Dance Games; Paul Rooyackers ; Hunter House

101 Movement Games for Children; Huberta Wiertsema; Hunter House

101 Rhythm Instrument Activities For Young Children; Abigail Flesch Connors; Gryphon House

Dancing Around the World; Nicholas Brasch; Longman

Dance for Infants; Jim Hall, A&C Black

Minibeasts

Previous experience

Experiencing living things is a key part of the early years curriculum, and a fascination with minibeasts is central to many children's interests. In the EYFS, children will probably have:

- watched and investigated minibeasts in gardens and outdoor spaces
- used bug collectors and magnifying glasses

and may also have:

- watched caterpillars turning into butterflies
- made a wormery
- made an ant farm
- watched slugs and snails
- gone on a minibeast hunt.

The responsive adult

In the early stages of working with these materials it is crucial to continue to observe the children. Only by doing this can you set developmentally appropriate challenges and provocations. The ideas listed here are offered as suggestions; the most exciting challenges will arise from children's own interests and motivations, which will only become apparent as you spend time with them, watching and joining them in their play. As you do this, you will be moving between the three interconnecting roles of observer, co-player, extender described below, and will be able to decide what you need to do next to take the learning forward. In three interconnecting roles, the responsive adult will be:

Observer

- observing
- listening
- interpreting

Co-player

- modelling
- playing alongside
- offering suggestions
- responding sensitively
- initiating with care!

Extender

- discussing ideas
- sharing thinking
- modelling new skills
- asking open questions
- being an informed extender
- instigating ideas and thoughts
- supporting children as they make links in learning
- making possibilities evident
- introducing new ideas and resources
- offering challenges and provocations

Offering challenges and provocations

In KS1 children may need to top up their experiences of minibeasts with further use of magnifying glasses, bug collectors and time to watch minibeasts in action in your outdoor area. Then start with simple challenges that reinforce positive attitudes to living things, and care in handling equipment.

- Find a magnifying glass and a clip board. Now can you explore and record the names of the living things that live in your outside area?

- Can you find some snails or slugs? Gently collect some and put them in an aquarium or a big plastic box. Watch what they do. Can you give them something they would like to eat? Find out what they need by looking in books or the internet. Put the creatures back where you found them after you have looked at them.

- Make an information book or poster about minibeasts that live in your school grounds. Use a camera, draw pictures or find some pictures on the internet.

- Work with some friends to look under stones and logs for very small insects, flies and beetles. Collect some and make a habitat for them in a plastic box. Handle them gently, and don't forget to look at where they were living, so you make the right sort of habitat.

- Put one of these words in Google Images 'minibeasts' 'caterpillars' 'slugs' 'butterflies' 'moths' 'spiders' and find out all you can about the minibeast of your choice.

- Make a minibeast quiz for your friends. Choose or draw some pictures of minibeasts and stick them on cards. Now challenge your friends to name them. You could make a game of Minibeast Snap, Minibeast Pairs or Minibeast Bingo.

- Make a habitat for Spiderman that will attract spiders. You need to think hard about what spiders like and where they live.

Ready for more?

♦ Work with some friends to make a minibeast habitat in your garden or school grounds. Research what to do by contacting local environmental groups, who may come to help you. Then look at the sort of minibeasts that live in your grounds and choose materials for their habitat that they will like. You can use stones, concrete slabs, guttering, wood, logs, sticks, leaves, moss and many other natural and man-made materials. Take some photos of the habitat as you build it, and then record the minibeasts that visit.

♦ Make a PowerPoint presentation of the photos of your habitat, and show the presentation to your friends, other classes, parents and even the whole school!

♦ Find out about how minibeasts reproduce. Do they lay eggs? If so, what do they look like and where could you find some? What to baby minibeasts look like? Which ones look like their parents and which ones have to change as they grow? What do baby minibeasts eat?

♦ Find out how to make an ant farm or a wormery, then make one for your classroom. Collect all the things you need, including a good container, before you collect the ants or worms.

♦ Send for a butterfly box from **www.greengardener. co.uk** and grow your own butterflies from caterpillars.

Materials

Educational suppliers have plenty of science resources that are ideal for minibeast work. Make sure you have plenty of magnifying glasses, bug boxes and collecting devices. You also need some plastic aquariums, and plastic boxes of all sizes.

Store these somewhere accessible so children can get them easily as they work.

You could also add some replica minibeasts that can be offered in small containers or baskets to inspire stories and environments — include insects, beetles, ants etc.

Websites

There are hundreds of minibeast sites and images on the internet, and these have downloadable leaflets of ideas and information, some for children, some for teachers:

www.ers.north-ayrshire.gov.uk/minibeasts

www.highlandschools-virtualib.org.uk tre.ngfl.gov.uk (Teacher Resource exchange)

www.ehsni.gov.uk environmental heritage site with booklets to download

www.nwt.org.uk for a Minibeasts.pdf leaflet

www.ypte.org.uk/docs/factsheets/env_facts/minibeasts Young People's Trust for the Environment with good information and activities

www.bbsrc.ac.uk/society/schools/primary/minibeast/ discovery2.pdf — a leaflet on Making Bug boxes

www.sutton.gov.uk or **www.ntseducation.org.uk** - for minibeast workpacks.

www.insectlore.co.uk have butterfly kits and lots of other insect resources and information about keeping and investigating insects, and **web.ukonline.co.uk/conker/pond-dip/tadpoles** has information on keeping tadpoles. These are just a few!

Books

Minibeasts (Amazing Life Cycles); George McGavin; Ticktock Media Ltd

Minibeasts (Foundations); Rachel Sparks-Linfield; A & C Black

Minibeasts; Siobhan Hardy; Collins Educational

Minibeasts (Hot Topics); Gerald Legg; Belitha Press Ltd

Slugs and Snails (Minibeasts); Claire Llewellyn; Franklin Watts

Spiders, Insects, and Minibeasts (Scary Creatures); Penny Clarke; Franklin Watts

Minibeasts (poems); Brian Moses; Macmillan Children's Books

Outdoor Fun and Games for Kids: Over 100 Activities for 3-11 Year Olds; Jane Kemp; Hamlyn

Outdoor Activities for Kids: Over 100, Practical Things to Do Outside; Clare Bradley; Lorenz Books

The Kid's Wildlife Book: Exploring Animal Worlds; Williamson Publishing

From Tadpole to Frog; Wendy Pfeffer; Harper Trophy

From Caterpillar to Butterfly; Deborah Heiligman; Harper Collins

The Very Hungry Caterpillar; Eric Carle; Picture Puffin

Growing things

Previous experience

Growing seeds, bulbs and plants is a part of every early years setting, and children should be familiar with digging, planting, growing and tending plants through some of these activities:

- digging activities in mud and compost
- using simple tools and equipment
- planting and growing seeds such as beans and flowers
- planting young plants in window boxes and tubs for decoration
- growing simple food plants such as beans, lettuce, cress, tomatoes
- growing bulbs indoors and outside
- making and playing in sensory gardens
- making gardens or helping to plant living willow or other garden plants for play and decoration.

The responsive adult

In the early stages of working with these materials it is crucial to continue to observe the children. Only by doing this can you set developmentally appropriate challenges and provocations. The ideas listed here are offered as suggestions; the most exciting challenges will arise from children's own interests and motivations, which will only become apparent as you spend time with them, watching and joining them in their play. As you do this, you will be moving between the three interconnecting roles of observer, co-player, extender described below, and will be able to decide what you need to do next to take the learning forward. In three interconnecting roles, the responsive adult will be:

Observer
- observing
- listening
- interpreting

Co-player
- modelling
- playing alongside
- offering suggestions
- responding sensitively
- initiating with care!

Extender
- discussing ideas
- sharing thinking
- modelling new skills
- asking open questions
- being an informed extender
- instigating ideas and thoughts
- supporting children as they make links in learning
- making possibilities evident
- introducing new ideas and resources
- offering challenges and provocations

Offering challenges and provocations

Growing plants is a good way to encourage pride in the school environment and to help develop a sense of responsibility. Children can be involved in small and larger projects from planting sunflowers to redesigning the whole school garden or making a forest school area. Here are some simple starters for independent work.

- Go for a walk in your school garden or grounds and take photos of all the different plants you see. Some of these may be weeds. When you have downloaded or printed your photos, use the library or the internet to find out what they are.

- Collect some seeds and pips from fruit and vegetables — apple and orange pips, tomato pips, melon seeds, avocado stones, anything you eat. Now collect some simple containers such as yogurt pots or plastic cups and try growing some of your seeds. They may take a long time to start growing, so be patient and find out how to look after them.

- While you are waiting for your seeds and pips to grow, design a plant pot, using a plastic pot and recycled materials.

- Look round your outdoor area and see if there are some places where you could grow plants for flowers or food. Make a plan, draw your ideas and see if your teachers can help you to grow some.

- Are there any trees in your school grounds? Photograph these and find out their names. Make a book for the school library with all the school trees in.

- Get some sunflower seeds and grow them. Have a contest to see who can grow the tallest one. When they have flowered, keep the seeds to feed the birds.

- Get some bulbs (if you buy them near Christmas, they will be cheaper!). Grow them in your classroom for flowers in the spring.

Ready for more?

- Find out about Living Willow by looking on the internet at www.livingwillow. fsnet.co.uk. Can you think of a way to raise some money to plant living willow in your school grounds?

- In the autumn, go outside and see how many different kinds of seeds you can find. Collect them in bags and label the bags, so you don't forget what they are. Now plant the seeds in different pots and see what grows.

- Get some plastic pots, a growbag and some vegetable seeds. What do you need to do to make a vegetable garden?

- Can you make a scarecrow for your garden, to stop the birds from eating your seeds? Collect some recycled materials and have a scarecrow competition to see who can make the best one.

- Find some old, clean towels and cut them up to fit in shallow containers. Make the towelling wet. Now sprinkle some of these seeds on the damp towelling — grass seed, cress, mustard, nasturtiums or peas. Watch what happens, taking photos every two days. Make a display of your experiments.

- Can you make a hanging basket from recycled materials? Look for some young plants - pansies, petunias, geraniums, lobelia etc to plant in your hanging basket. After the summer, plant your basket again with bulbs, winter pansies or herbs for the winter.

Materials, websites, books and other references

Materials

Strong tools are essential for school use - invest in some good ones specially made for children www.brio.co.uk will give you stockists. Or buy small versions of adult tools (usually labelled for women!). More and more of the educational suppliers are stocking garden tools, so check these or your local consortium group for prices. TTS Group www.ttsgroup.co.uk have a range of tools and barrows etc.

Ask parents and friends for used plant pots, plant saucers and other recycled materials. They may also be willing to donate excess seedlings and cuttings from plants. Grow bags are a cheap way of gardening with children (choose ones with contents from sustainable sources). Provide a digging area if you can, where children can explore the fun of just digging.

Websites

Try Google to find out about plants and flowers, and don't forget that some weeds have lovely flowers and leaves, and are also free. Find out about quick growing and child friendly plants from the Royal Horticultural Society www.rhs.org.uk and click on 'plant finder'. The BBC www.bbc.co.uk - has a Gardening with Children section.

www.sustainweb.org — growing plants (planting seeds such as fruit pips and stones

www.standards.dfes.gov.uk/schemes2/science — DfES guidance on growing things

www-saps.plantsci.cam.ac.uk — download leaflet on growing seeds

www.naturegrid.org.uk — QCA ideas on growing things

www.thekidsgarden.co.uk — recycling for kids

or try www.ltl.org.uk — the Learning Through Landscapes website

The Little Book of Growing Things (from www.acblack.com) has hundreds of ideas for school gardening, many of them free or cheap options.

Books

Nature's Playground; Fiona Danks; Frances Lincoln Publishers

Great Gardens for Kids; Clare Matthews; Hamlyn

Gardening with Children; Kim Wilde; Collins

Harry's Garden; Kim Wilde; Collins Educational

How To Make a Scarecrow; Kim Wilde; Collins Educational

Roots, Shoots, Buckets and Boots; Sharon Lovejoy; Workman

Usborne Starting Gardening; Sue Johnson; E.D.C. Publishing

The Gardening Book; Jane Bull; Dorling Kindersley

Mark-making and writing

Previous experience

By the time they reach Year 1, most children will have had extensive opportunities to use mark-making materials for a wide range of purposes and in many different contexts. They will have made marks with everything from fingers and toes to water colour crayons as part of:

- role-play
- activities in a graphics area
- out of doors in gardens and other spaces
- in construction
- when working with clay, dough and other malleable materials
- free play on a range of surfaces
- playing in mud, water, snow
- making signs, notices and labels
- making messages and writing letters.

The responsive adult

In the early stages of working with these materials it is crucial to continue to observe the children. Only by doing this can you set developmentally appropriate challenges and provocations. The ideas listed here are offered as suggestions; the most exciting challenges will arise from children's own interests and motivations, which will only become apparent as you spend time with them, watching and joining them in their play. As you do this, you will be moving between the three interconnecting roles of observer, co-player, extender described below, and will be able to decide what you need to do next to take the learning forward. In three interconnecting roles, the responsive adult will be:

Observer

- observing
- listening
- interpreting

Co-player

- modelling
- playing alongside
- offering suggestions
- responding sensitively
- initiating with care!

Extender

- discussing ideas
- sharing thinking
- modelling new skills
- asking open questions
- being an informed extender
- instigating ideas and thoughts
- supporting children as they make links in learning
- making possibilities evident
- introducing new ideas and resources
- offering challenges and provocations

Offering challenges and provocations

Portable mark-making kits make it much easier for children to draw and write outside, in places of their own choice, and they are particularly attractive to boys. Replenish these kits regularly with attractive and colourful materials to stimulate children's imaginations. The kits can be used for both adult-led and child-initiated activities, while children are:

- role-playing — to develop and record narratives, or to make maps and signs
- constructing — to make plans, write lists and instructions
- investigating — to record experiments, collect information
- being creative — in making marks of all sorts
- practising and extending what they are learning in the classroom.

- Can you plan and set up a treasure hunt for your friends? You could bury treasure in sand, or make a treasure hunt round the whole outdoor area. Plan your treasure hunt first, then write the instructions for your friends to follow. See if you can hide each clue in a different place.

- Can you lay a trail with chalk for your friends to follow? Make marks or arrows on the ground or on walls, paths and fences. Give yourself a five minute start before they follow you!

- Make a notice board for your outside area or the playground. Hang it on a fence or wall, and use chalk, pencil or felt pens to write messages for your friends. You could announce a play or parade, invite them to play a game with you, or leave a message in code or secret writing.

- Look up 'prayer flags' in Google Images. Can you make some flags with writing or messages on them. You will need some strips of fabric and some paint. Old sheets make good flags if you tear them in strips. You could start by making name flags for everyone in your class.

Ready for more?

♦ Make some posters about the animals, birds, minibeasts and plants in your school garden or outdoor area. Can you find a way of making your posters waterproof, so they can be displayed outside?

♦ Find a notebook or diary and use this to make an Outdoor Diary of the school play area or garden. Take turns to write and draw about the things you see. You could include:

  • the weather
  • birds, insects and animals you see
  • plants, flowers, leaves
  • sounds you hear
  • the clouds
  • signs of the seasons
  • the sorts of games you played
  • photos as well as drawings.

♦ Make a collection of weather and wildlife poems. You could start with some from books and the internet, and then write some more of your own.

♦ Can you design and make a book of games that can be played outside? Start with the ones you know, then ask your family and friends if they know any more.

♦ Can you be a pavement artist and make a picture on the path, playground or patio? Use chalk and make sure you do it where you will not be walked on!

♦ Find a camera and use it to help you make an outdoor alphabet book with photos and words. Design a good cover for your book.

Materials, websites, books and other references

Materials

Try www.newitts.com - for playground chalk, cones and markers for games.

Websites

www.scienceyear.com/under11s/playground — download a free leaflet with ideas for painting your own playground games

www.playquest.co.uk — make playground markings and have some good ideas in the photos on their website, as well as giant chess and draught pieces

www.linepainting.net — more ideas for markings

www.pioneer.cwc.net/playgroundpals.htm — takes you to a whole list of sites with ideas for playground games

www.worcestershire.gov.uk/home/09_play_mark.pdf — download a free leaflet on making playground markings

www.sunclocks.com - for some pictures of paintings on a playground

Look at users.skynet.be/J.Beever/pave.htm for some amazing 3D pavement drawings.

Download a really nice guide to making nature notebooks from www.nwf.org/kidzone

Google Images

Try searching for:

  • pavement art
  • graffiti
  • mural
  • pavement art.

Books

Some Books about outdoor environments:

Environments for Outdoor Play: A Practical Guide to Making Space for Children; Theresa Casey; Paul Chapman Educational Publishing

Ecoart!: Earth-friendly Art and Craft Experiences for 3 to 9 Year Olds; Lauri Carlson; Williamson Publishing

Playing Outside; Helen Bilton; David Fulton Publishers

Outdoor Play in the Early Years; Helen Bilton; David Fulton Publishers

Creating a Space to Grow; Gail Ryder-Richardson; David Fulton Publishers

Playing and Learning Outdoors; Jan White; Routledge

Sidewalk Chalk: Outdoor Fun and Games; Jamie Kyle McGillian; Sterling Juvenile

A Piece of Chalk; Jennifer A. Ericsson; Roaring Brook Press

Squeaky Chalk; Joy Sikorski; Random House

The Jumbo Book of Outdoor Art; Irene Luxbacher; Kids Can Press

The Little Book of Writing and The Little Book of Props for Writing; A & C Black

Dens and shelters

Previous experience

Making dens is a favourite occupation for children in Nursery and Reception. Most children will have had experience of using drapes, sticks, pegs and other things to make dens in the gardens of their settings:

- under climbing frames
- against walls
- under trees, in bushes and hedges
- in tents and under clothes airer.

They will also have used drapes for:

- dressing up
- wrapping themselves and other objects
- making tents, wigwams, houses
- dancing
- using drapes as a home-made parachute.

The responsive adult

In the early stages of working with these materials it is crucial to continue to observe the children. Only by doing this can you set developmentally appropriate challenges and provocations. The ideas listed here are offered as suggestions; the most exciting challenges will arise from children's own interests and motivations, which will only become apparent as you spend time with them, watching and joining them in their play. As you do this, you will be moving between the three interconnecting roles of observer, co-player, extender described below, and will be able to decide what you need to do next to take the learning forward. In three interconnecting roles, the responsive adult will be:

Observer

- observing
- listening
- interpreting

Co-player

- modelling
- playing alongside
- offering suggestions
- responding sensitively
- initiating with care!

Extender

- discussing ideas
- sharing thinking
- modelling new skills
- asking open questions
- being an informed extender
- instigating ideas and thoughts
- supporting children as they make links in learning
- making possibilities evident
- introducing new ideas and resources
- offering challenges and provocations

Offering challenges and provocations

Offer all sorts of den building materials to the children — canes, sticks, fabrics (lightweight ones are easiest to manage), clips and pegs, string and rope, boxes and cardboard.

- Can you make a wigwam or tepee? You may need to look on the internet to see how they are made.

- Can you make a shelter with:
  - three vertical sides?
  - four sloping sides?
  - six triangular sides?

- Can you make a den from branches, sticks and leaves?

- Can you make a den from boxes? Can you make it waterproof and windproof? Take some photos to show what you did. Make a display of your photos.

- Put 'building dens' in Google Images for some ideas.

- Can you make a den for an animal? Look on Google 'animal dens'.

- Can you make a den from sticks and plastic? Take care when you are using plastic. Can you make the den so dark that you can use a torch inside?

- Get some plain fabric (old sheets are good for this, so ask your parents if they have any). Now decorate the fabric before you make a 'designer den' with it. You could use:
  - felt pens
  - fabric crayons
  - tie dye
  - printing with objects
  - spray painting with dilute food colouring and hand sprays
  - sticking on patches of different fabrics, natural objects such as leaves, or buttons, sequins and beads.

- Can you find two points outside where you could tie the ends of a rope? If you can, try making a den by draping a big sheet or blanket over the rope and putting stones on the edges to keep the tent open.

Ready for more?

♦ Make a den from plastic carrier bags. Can you think of a way to fix the bags together? You could use:

- silver duct tape

- brown parcel tape

- a big needle and thread

- staples.

Which works best? Work in groups to trial and evaluate each method.

♦ What makes the best framework for a den? Is it:

- canes?

- branches?

- broom handles?

♦ Can you make a wind-proof AND waterproof den?

♦ Can you make a den with more than one room? Is it big enough for furniture?

♦ Look at how a pop-up tent is made. Can you make a den using the same method? What could you use?

♦ Can you make a shelter from recycled materials?

♦ Use the internet to find out about 'Living Willow' and how you can plant a living willow den. Could you plant one in your school garden or grounds?

Materials

Children need lots of flexible resources to make dens and shelters, and many of these are cheap or even free. Try collecting some of these:

- sticks, canes and bamboo

- cable ties, string, tape of all sorts

- fabric sheets (lightweight ones such as sheeting or sari fabric work well)

- pegs, clips, elastic, hair 'scrunchies'

- plastic sheeting (such as cheap dust-sheets), light tarpaulins, bubble wrap

- plastic carrier bags and bin bags

- cardboard boxes

- cardboard sheeting from the sides of boxes and cartons

Ask parents and local businesses to help by offering you packaging materials.

Google Images

Search for **tree house** for some staggering examples, or

- den

- kids playhouse

- hut

- nest.

- house in the woods

Materials, websites, books and other references

Books

The Best Den Ever; Anne Cassidy; Franklin Watts

Children's Special Places: Exploring the Role of Forts, Dens and Bush Houses in Middle Childhood; David Sobel; Wayne State University Press

Foxes and Their Dens; Martha E. H. Rustad; Capstone Press

A Den, a Tree, a Nest Is Best; Katharine Kenah; School Specialty Publishing

The Den; Adam Stower; Bloomsbury Publishing

Tree Houses You Can Actually Build; David Stiles; Houghton Mifflin

Build Your Own Fantasy Treehouse; David Parfitt; David & Charles

Making Make-believe: Fun Props, Costumes and Creative Play Ideas; MaryAnn F. Kohl; Gryphon House

A Place to Talk Series; A & C Black

Weather and seasons

Previous experience

Projects on the weather and the seasons form a central part of the curriculum for science and knowledge of the world in the early years. Children may have had some of these experiences:

- looking at seasonal plants and flowers
- watching what animals and birds do
- watching and recording the weather
- playing out of doors in different seasons and weathers
- talking about clothing and footwear
- cooking seasonal food
- visiting parks and woodlands in different seasons
- using their senses to explore different weather and times of year
- seasonal songs, rhymes and poems.

The responsive adult

In the early stages of working with these materials it is crucial to continue to observe the children. Only by doing this can you set developmentally appropriate challenges and provocations. The ideas listed here are offered as suggestions; the most exciting challenges will arise from children's own interests and motivations, which will only become apparent as you spend time with them, watching and joining them in their play. As you do this, you will be moving between the three interconnecting roles of observer, co-player, extender described below, and will be able to decide what you need to do next to take the learning forward. In three interconnecting roles, the responsive adult will be:

Observer

- observing
- listening
- interpreting

Co-player

- modelling
- playing alongside
- offering suggestions
- responding sensitively
- initiating with care!

Extender

- discussing ideas
- sharing thinking
- modelling new skills
- asking open questions
- being an informed extender
- instigating ideas and thoughts
- supporting children as they make links in learning
- making possibilities evident
- introducing new ideas and resources
- offering challenges and provocations

Offering challenges and provocations

- What season is it now? How do you know? Use a camera to record some signs of the season.

- Make a weather chart for a week. Decide on some symbols for each sort of weather and use these to record the weather every day. You can find the TV weather symbols on the BBC weather site **www.bbc.co.uk/weather.**

- Can you make a book with ideas for games to play in each of the four seasons? Get your friends to play the games and take photos of them to illustrate your book.

- Do you know which flowers bloom in each season? Could you make a chart to show this?

- Go outside and look at the sky. What can you see? Watch the sky for fifteen minutes. How does it change? Make a list of all the things you saw happening in the sky as you watched.

- Can you invent a rain catcher using recycled materials? Draw your design, then make the rain catcher and leave it outside to catch the rain. How well does it work? Could you improve it?

- Start a bird watching diary for your class to use. Take turns to watch the birds every day and record what you all see. Use books and the internet to find out which birds visit your garden or school grounds.

- Birds will come if you make some bird feeders. Find out how to do this, and remember to feed the birds every day, even in the summer.

- Make a book about your favourite season. Paint a cover using colours that match the season.

Ready for more?

◆ Can you design a weather mobile that responds to wind, rain and sun? Make your mobile and hang it up outside.

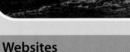

◆ Can you make a weather station? Decide what you need to measure and collect. Remember that you need to measure wind, rain, temperature, sunshine. How can you do this? Use the internet to help.

◆ Make a sundial in your garden or grounds. Look at **www.bbc.co.uk/norfolk/kids** or **www.nmm.ac.uk** and search 'sundial'. Both sites have instructions and templates to print out.

◆ Go outside and collect some natural materials — leaves, seeds, petals, twigs. Can you use these to make a seasonal collage? You could weave them into netting, or stick them on card or fabric. How could you protect your collage so you can hang it outside?

◆ Try this on a windy day. Go outside and see if you can measure how strong the wind is in different parts of the playground or school grounds. What can you use to measure the wind? You may need a friend to help. Record what you find out, using a camera.

◆ Find out how to press flowers. Make a flower press and press some seasonal flowers to make greeting cards, gift tags or calendars. Always ask before picking flowers, even weeds belong to someone!

Materials

Watching and recording the weather is a simple activity that really keeps children in touch with the natural world. You don't need an expensive weather chart or station just a routine for watching and a system for recording.

■ Photos are a really good way of recording the weather and the seasons. Encourage the children to take photos from the same place every day or during each season. Then you can make slide shows or photo books.

■ Make a habit of watching or listening to the weather forecast and checking whether what is forecast is what really happens.

■ Hang up simple objects that will alert the children to the weather — CDs, streamers, windsocks, prayer flags, metal pans to catch the sound of water, windmills, sundials or an unbreakable mirror on the floor to reflect the sky.

Research and provide some shelters for extreme weather — bright sun, cold winds, showers. gazebos and tents are good ways of enabling children to be outside in all weathers.

Google Images

For some really good, colourful photos try:

• seasons
• sun
• wind
• rain
• clouds
• storms
• hurricane.

Materials, websites, books and other references

Websites

There are lots of internet sites for making a weather station, but some sites really need adult help —

www.fi.edu/weather and **www.bbc.co.uk/tyne/weather** for weather station instructions

www.bbc.co.uk/weather/weatherwise/activities for useful information for adults and children

fun.familyeducation.com/Children's-science-activities/weather to find the activity 'rain in a bag'.

Books

The Kid's Book of Weather Forecasting; Mark Breen; Williamson Publishing Company

Winter/Spring/Autumn/Summer; Nature Activities for Children; Irmgard Kutsch; Floris Books

Weather Detectives; Mark Eubank; Gibbs Smith

Crafts for Kids Who Are Learning about Weather; Kathy Ross; Millbrook Press

The Wind Blew; Pat Hutchins; Aladdin

What Makes the Wind?; Laurence Santrey; Troll Communications

Petals, leaves, feathers and stones

Previous experience

The use of natural materials in the Foundation Stage is widespread — in art, craft, construction, science and technology. Children should have had wide experience of using these materials both in free play and in adult supported tasks and activities such as:

- collecting and discussing natural materials in free play, and during walks and visits

- making constructions and other creations from sticks, stones, leaves, shells and petals

- using sticks, leaves and feathers to make hangings and collages

- using sticks, stones etc to represent other objects — money, gifts, tickets, tokens — and to count and sort.

The responsive adult

In the early stages of working with these materials it is crucial to continue to observe the children. Only by doing this can you set developmentally appropriate challenges and provocations. The ideas listed here are offered as suggestions; the most exciting challenges will arise from children's own interests and motivations, which will only become apparent as you spend time with them, watching and joining them in their play. As you do this, you will be moving between the three interconnecting roles of observer, co-player, extender described below, and will be able to decide what you need to do next to take the learning forward. In three interconnecting roles, the responsive adult will be:

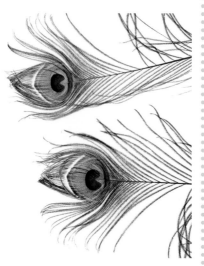

Observer

- observing
- listening
- interpreting

Co-player

- modelling
- playing alongside
- offering suggestions
- responding sensitively
- initiating with care!

Extender

- discussing ideas
- sharing thinking
- modelling new skills
- asking open questions
- being an informed extender
- instigating ideas and thoughts
- supporting children as they make links in learning
- making possibilities evident
- introducing new ideas and resources
- offering challenges and provocations

Offering challenges and provocations

Collect a range of longer lasting natural objects that can be used for construction, sorting and creative play — sticks, sawn logs, bark, compost, stones, pebbles and shells, seasonal items such as conkers and nuts, hay and straw. Add some more ephemeral objects such as flowers, petals, feathers, leaves, grass, seaweed, moss etc.

- Can you make a garden on a plate or a saucer? Go outside and see what you can collect to make your garden.

- Try painting and writing with natural materials — feathers, sticks, moss or flowers — which are best for writing with, which are best for pictures?

- Go for a walk round your outdoor area or garden. Take a carrier bag with you and see how many natural objects you can find. When you have finished, sort your collection out and photograph it.

- Look carefully at your collection with a magnifying glass. What can you see? Record all the tiny things you find.

- Find 25 stones or pebbles. Set these out in a line from the biggest to the smallest. Take a photo or draw your line. Now reorganise the pebbles by weight. Draw or photograph the new line. Is it different? Now organise the pebbles by colour or texture.

- Find a crayon or coloured pencil. Go outside and see if you can find something that is exactly the same colour as your crayon or pencil. Now try with another colour.

- Find some leaves. Sort them into different shapes and sizes. How many different sorts of leaves are there? Look in books and see if you can find out what the different shapes are called.

- Collect some sticks, stones, leaves and other natural materials. Get some wool or string and make a hanging with natural objects, by tying them onto a length of string. Find a place outside to display your hangings.

Ready for more?

◆ Use conkers, acorns, fir cones and other nuts or seeds to make sequences and repeating patterns.

◆ Can you find out about Rangoli Patterns? Look on Google images 'rangoli'. Use natural materials such as sand, pebbles, petals and leaves to make Rangoli patterns. There is an example on this page.

◆ Find some leaves or stones. Now can you mix paints that are exactly the same colours as your leaves and stones? Use your colours to make a painting of the leaves and stones and display them together.

◆ Work with four friends. Go outside and collect or dig up some stones. Wash the stones and each choose the one you like best. Do a pencil, charcoal or pastel drawing of your favourite stone and make an exhibition. See if other children can match the stones to the drawings.

◆ Look up 'Andy Goldsworthy' on Google images. Click on some of the images to find out how this artist uses flowers, stones and wood to make art works. Have a go yourselves!

◆ In winter, go for a walk and collect dead seed heads, skeleton leaves, grasses and other natural objects. Make a display. If you made a display of the natural objects of summer, would it look different?

Materials

Try to collect some baskets or boxes of stones, leaves, nuts, feathers, cones and other natural objects — keep these fresh by removing the old ones and replacing with collections from walks, visits, holidays and so on.

Always encourage children to pick up natural materials for the collection, and ask them to bring a shell, pebble, cone, leaf or a piece of driftwood from their holidays and you'll soon have a collection!

The message about collecting natural objects should always be "If it isn't fixed on, it is likely to be OK. If it is fixed on — ask!"

Buy pot pourri, polished pebbles, glass beads from bargain shops. Ask local florists or market traders for 'past their sell by' flowers to use for Rangoli and other art works.

Provide small containers, string and netting, shallow trays, plastic plates for creations and gardens. Offer peat and sand as a base for artwork.

Google Images

Try typing in:

- stone wall
- natural art
- art from nature
- Andy Goldsworthy
- natural collage
- pebble art
- painted stone
- rangoli
- petals
- leaves.

Websites

Look up 'Rangoli' on the internet and find out about this form of art, originally found on doorsteps. You can also download versions of rangoli patterns to use as bases for your creations with real petals, leaves, sand etc.

Books

Sharing Nature with Children; Joseph Cornell; Dawn Publications

Arts in the School Grounds; Brian Keaney; Learning Through Landscapes

Hands-on Nature; Jenepher Lingelbach; University Press of New England

Engaging Places; Commission for Architecture and the Built Environment (CABE)

Challenge of the Urban School Site; Learning through Landscapes

Nature's Playground; Fiona Danks; Frances Lincoln

Ecoart!; Lauri Carlson; Williamson Publishing

Bats, balls and beanbags

Previous experience

Throughout the Foundation Stage, children will have played with a range of different sized balls in both adult and child-initiated activities. They will have:

- patted
- bounced
- kicked
- rolled
- thrown and caught balls.

They may have had less experience of bats, which require a far greater degree of co-ordination and control.

The responsive adult

In the early stages of working with these materials it is crucial to continue to observe the children. Only by doing this can you set developmentally appropriate challenges and provocations. The ideas listed here are offered as suggestions; the most exciting challenges will arise from children's own interests and motivations, which will only become apparent as you spend time with them, watching and joining them in their play. As you do this, you will be moving between the three interconnecting roles of observer, co-player, extender described below, and will be able to decide what you need to do next to take the learning forward. In three interconnecting roles, the responsive adult will be:

Observer

- observing
- listening
- interpreting

Co-player

- modelling
- playing alongside
- offering suggestions
- responding sensitively
- initiating with care!

Extender

- discussing ideas
- sharing thinking
- modelling new skills
- asking open questions
- being an informed extender
- instigating ideas and thoughts
- supporting children as they make links in learning
- making possibilities evident
- introducing new ideas and resources
- offering challenges and provocations

Offering challenges and provocations

In order for children to develop their skills further, there is plenty of scope for continued free play with bats and balls, where children can explore at their own pace, supported by sympathetic adults. Some children in Year 1 may still find it difficult to catch a ball, so try using something that travels through the air at a slower pace, such as:

- a balloon
- a balloon wrapped in a headscarf
- a beanbag
- a 'koosh ball'.

● Make a collection of balls of different sizes. How many can you find? How can you measure which is biggest and which is smallest?

● Can you make up some new ball games, using your new collection of different balls?

● Can you invent some games by combining balls with other things such as:

- plastic buckets
- playground chalk
- plastic bottles, empty or filled with sand or water
- guttering and drainpipes
- wire coat hangers to make hoops in grass areas for balls to go through?

● Write some instructions for playing these games.

● Look in books and on the internet to find out how to play new ball games. Try some of them out.

● Invent some games for bats and balls. Can you make up:

- a target game
- a game using numbers
- a passing game
- a team game
- a 'tag' game
- a parachute game?

Remember, all the games must use at least one ball and at least one bat. Play the games to check they really work!

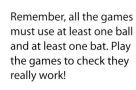

Ready for more?

♦ Find out how balls were made in the past. Look on the Internet and in books. Ask your relatives and older people you know. Contact your local museum or sports club to see if they can tell you anything.

♦ Experiment with making a ball. What can you use? Recycled materials work well. You could try using:

- elastic bands
- newspaper
- string
- stuffed plastic bags
- old CDs or postcards
- tin cans or bottles.

Look on Google Images 'making balls' for some help and ideas.

♦ Throw your ball against a wall or into the air. While it is in the air, clap you hands, then catch the ball again. Try again — can you clap twice, or three times? Can you clap your hands above your head, or behind your back before catching the ball again?

♦ Have a contest with your friends. Who can clap the most times after throwing the ball in the air, and before they catch it? Can they throw the ball, turn round, then catch it again? Record the results and then see if you can beat the record.

♦ Can you use more than one ball to juggle? Some people can juggle with three or four balls. Find out how to do it.

Materials

Outdoor PE equipment is easy to find and cheap in educational supply and consortium catalogues. If you want some different ideas, try **ascoeducational.co.uk.** You could also add:

- home made bean bags, beach balls; ribbon sticks
- playground chalk, black or white boards and markers
- trundle wheels
- buckets
- a parachute.

Google images

Some suggestions for words to search:

- **playground games**
- **Victorian playground games**
- **skittles** or other games.

Websites

Google web for '**make your own skittles**' or the name of any other game will give you instructions on making your own equipment and games.

www.playgroundfun.org.uk is a site for children with a range of different games and tips for adults on using them in school.

www.llanddulas.conwy.sch.uk has some good pictures and instructions for playing some of the best playground games.

Materials, websites, books and other references

Books

Outdoor Fun and Games for Kids; 100+ Activities for 3-11s; Jane Kemp; Hamlyn

Outdoor Activities for Kids; 100+ Things to Do Outside; Clare Brad; Lorenz Books

Creating a Space to Grow; Gail Ryder-Richardson; David Fulton

Primary Playground Games; Cat Weatherill; Scholastic

The Little Book of Playground Games; Simon MacDonald; A & C Black

The Little Book of Parachute Play; Clare Beswick; A & C Black

The Jump Rope Book; Elizabeth Loredo; Workman Publishing

EarthFriendly Outdoor Fun: Make Fabulous Games, Gardens, and Other Projects from Reusable Objects; George Pfiffner; Jossey Bass

Numbers

Previous experience

Children may have already had experience of using numbers out of doors in:

- collecting and counting objects they see, find and are shown in the environment

- recording scores for games

- writing numbers with chalk or paint

- singing and chanting counting and number songs and games such as *What's the Time Mr Wolf?*

- playing counting games marked on the ground, or counting in ring games

- playing games with natural objects

- in pretend shopping, home play and other roles

- counting seeds as they plant them, measuring the growth of plants.

The responsive adult

In the early stages of working with these materials it is crucial to continue to observe the children. Only by doing this can you set developmentally appropriate challenges and provocations. The ideas listed here are offered as suggestions; the most exciting challenges will arise from children's own interests and motivations, which will only become apparent as you spend time with them, watching and joining them in their play. As you do this, you will be moving between the three interconnecting roles of observer, co-player, extender described below, and will be able to decide what you need to do next to take the learning forward. In three interconnecting roles, the responsive adult will be:

Observer

- observing
- listening
- interpreting

Co-player

- modelling
- playing alongside
- offering suggestions
- responding sensitively
- initiating with care!

Extender

- discussing ideas
- sharing thinking
- modelling new skills
- asking open questions
- being an informed extender
- instigating ideas and thoughts
- supporting children as they make links in learning
- making possibilities evident
- introducing new ideas and resources
- offering challenges and provocations

Offering challenges and provocations

Children should continue all the activities they have enjoyed in Reception, with added challenge of bigger numbers and more adventurous ideas. Children in Key Stage 1 can work in pairs and groups to explore and invent games and use numbers.

- Find some playground chalk and draw some long, straight lines on the ground outside. Find out which line is longest by measuring and counting. Now draw some wiggly lines and find out which is the longest one of these.

- Do this with a friend or two. Find a stopwatch or timer and time yourselves doing these things:

  - running round the playground
  - scoring three goals with a football
  - hopping round in a big circle
  - touching every tree in the garden
  - finding something small and green.

  Find a way to record your times.

- Find some bean bags and play a counting game outside. Write your scores on the ground with chalk.

- Get two buckets and some small balls (ping pong balls are good fun). Make up a counting game with the buckets and balls.

- Use a water tray or builder's tray and make a fishing games. Make the fish from waterproof recycled materials, write numbers on them with a waterproof marker, and use small strainers or nets to catch the fish.

- How many of these can you find or see in your garden in five minutes?

  - minibeasts — such as ants, snails and spiders
  - birds — flying, perching, eating
  - flowers — on weeds, bushes, trees or hedges as well as on garden plants
  - vehicles — cars, bikes, aeroplanes, vans, buses, lorries.

  Record your findings in any way you choose.

Ready for more?

♦ Make a list of all the playground games you know. Now make a chart and find out which are the five most popular games in your class. Play these games, take photos and make a book with instructions.

♦ Find some skittles of small playground cones. Mark these with numbers and make up a game to play with them. Design a score sheet to use, then test the game with your friends.

♦ Make a target on the ground or the wall, number the target circles, and use bean bags or wet sponges to play a throwing game. Write your scores on a whiteboard.

♦ Do a garden count. Plan the count first and make a recording chart. Include some of these in your count:

   • trees, bushes and plants

   • places to sit

   • habitats for animals, insects, birds

   • risky or dangerous places.

   You could add photos or a plan to your results and make a display.

♦ Find a stopwatch or timer and challenge a group of friends to do some outdoor tasks against the clock. You decide what to ask them to do. Include all sorts of challenges, not just running. You could get them to search, dig, construct, work with sand or water, or make something.

♦ Make a set of giant dominoes, number bean bags or draughts and make an outdoor playing board with chalk or paint.

Materials

Counting and number activities mostly involve taking resources from inside into the garden. Here are some ways you could do this:

■ put some chalk, white boards and other counting items in a basket or bag for outdoor activities;

■ have a small trolley or tiered vegetable basket for equipment;

■ provide bags, small backpacks, belts with clips etc for writing implements, games kit such as balls and other small equipment.

Google images

• bamboo	• counting games
• children's games	• giant dominoes
• parachute	• giant chess
• number games	• outdoor games

Websites

www.bbc.co.uk/parenting/play_and_do/primary_outdoor for outdoor games for 7-11 year olds

www.funandgames.org and click through to games for hundreds of different games to play

www.greatgardengames.com a site that sells big size garden games - good for ideas

www.gameskidsplay.net games compendium site

www.woodlands-junior.kent.sch.uk a school site with playground games including a giant version of Connect

www.find-me-a-gift.co.uk has a great photo of a giant Ludo set you could use as an idea and

Materials, websites, books and other references

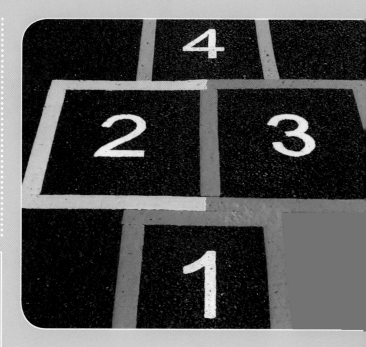

Books

Primary Playground Games; Cat Weatherill; Scholastic

Get Out! Outdoor Activities Kids Can Enjoy Anywhere; Hallie Warshaw; Sterling Juvenile, US

The Little Book of Playground Games; Simon MacDonald; A&C Black

The Little Book of Maths Outdoors; A&C Black

Juggling; Clive Gifford; Usborne

Making Waves: Exciting Parachute Games; Helen Sonnet; LDA

Great Big Book of Children's Games: 450+ Indoor & Outdoor Games for Kids; Derba Wise; McGraw Hill

The Outrageous Outdoor Games Book: 133 Group Projects, Games, and Activities; Bob Gregson; Fearon

Go Figure!: Prizewinning book about numbers; Johnny Ball; DK

Stories

Previous experience

There will be very few children who will not, at some time in the Foundation Stage, have role-played *We're Going on a Bear Hunt* outside. They may also have:

- built houses for the Three Pigs

- made a beanstalk for Jack to climb

- played out Red Riding Hood's journey to Grandmother's house

- been the Three Bears, walking through the forest

- planned a trip to the Moon like the little bear in *Whatever Next*?

- been transformed into a Superhero story.

The challenge for KS1 teachers is to:

- support children in expanding the challenge and complexity of their role-play stories

- identify new stories for telling out of doors.

The responsive adult

In the early stages of working with these materials it is crucial to continue to observe the children. Only by doing this can you set developmentally appropriate challenges and provocations. The ideas listed here are offered as suggestions; the most exciting challenges will arise from children's own interests and motivations, which will only become apparent as you spend time with them, watching and joining them in their play. As you do this, you will be moving between the three interconnecting roles of observer, co-player, extender described below, and will be able to decide what you need to do next to take the learning forward. In three interconnecting roles, the responsive adult will be:

Observer

- observing
- listening
- interpreting

Co-player

- modelling
- playing alongside
- offering suggestions
- responding sensitively
- initiating with care!

Extender

- discussing ideas
- sharing thinking
- modelling new skills
- asking open questions
- being an informed extender
- instigating ideas and thoughts
- supporting children as they make links in learning
- making possibilities evident
- introducing new ideas and resources
- offering challenges and provocations

Offering challenges and provocations

Encourage children to innovate and invent new versions of well known stories — for example:

- Can you invent a new 'Bear Hunt' story — about a Lion Hunt, a Dragon Hunt, a Dinosaur Hunt, a Butterfly Hunt?

- Someone else is in the Three Bears' House. Who might it be? What will happen next?

- The Superheroes are planning a concert for the children in the hospital. What happens when they all show off their powers?

- Can you make some props and costumes for your story? Use recycled materials and see what you can do.

- Make some scenery for your story from shower curtains and big boxes.

- Now photograph or video your story and make a computer presentation or a photo story book. Or you could laminate the photos and make them into an outdoor wall story mounted on a wall.

- Create a performance area where you can act out your story with or without an audience.

- Plan and build an outside den or area specially for stories. How many people can fit in your story space?

- Design and build some spaces for stories outside, where you and your friends can go to read or write stories out of doors.

  - How will you make it comfortable?
  - How will you keep it warm and dry?
  - Who will choose and look after the books?
  - What will you provide for children who want to write or draw their own stories?

Ready for more?

◆ Can you make a collection of stories about pirates? Now can you make a place outside where you can play these stories? Can you make a boat?

◆ Can you make an outside listening area where children can go to listen to stories on CD or tape?

◆ Prop boxes help you to tell stories. Can you make a 'prop box' for one of your favourite stories, such as *The Bear Hunt*, *Cinderella* or *Finding Nemo*?

◆ Have a 'Story of the week'. Make an outdoor prop box for the story.

◆ Find some stories that you can tell in a builder's tray or a big seed tray of compost, using small world people and animals. Photograph or film your stories and write your own script.

◆ Look for some stories about eggs. Do some nest building outside as you retell the story.

◆ Can you find stories about monsters, or robots, or scarecrows, or castles. Design scenery for retelling them out of doors.

◆ Recreate some stories about growing things and nature, and recreate these out of doors in trays and boxes.

◆ Find a way of making an island or a forest outside. Use this as the basis for telling stories.

◆ Work in groups to produce a concert for outdoor performance. Choose a theme such as Traditional Stories, Fantasy, Animal Stories, Adventure Islands.

Materials, websites, books and other references

Materials

Drama outdoors needs inspiration, but this doesn't need to be complicated or directive. Try:

■ a basket of fabrics (drapes and lengths of material) with pegs and other fastenings, wigs, hats, belts and other props

■ a backpack of story based materials — the children could collect these, or suggest items to add, stories to include etc

■ use puppets and soft toys to inspire story telling outside

■ set up story situations in pop-up tents, shelters, sheds and dens

■ offer small world animals and people for story making outside.

Google Images

• outdoor performance area

• pop up tent

• kids drama

Websites

www.literacytrust.org.uk or www.standards.dfes.gov.uk/parentalinvolvement/pics/pics_storysacks for information on story sacks

www.storysack.com is Neil Griffiths' site for his ready made story sacks for the primary age range

www.kidsonthenet.org.uk — a creative writing site for children

www.oakthorpe.enfield.sch.uk/tour — a school with an outdoor stage

www.playforce.co.uk or www.cookson-mcnally.co.uk/playspaces — both companies supply performance areas for schools, you could look here for ideas.

Books

101 Drama Games for Children, and 101 More Drama Games for Children; Paul Rooyackers; Hunter House

Children Engaging with Drama; a downloadable version of the National Theatre report on their work with primary schools (website-archive2.nt-online.org)

How to Write a Play; Cyntha Rothman; Harcourt

Break a Leg! The Kids' Guide to Acting and Stagecraft; Lise Friedman; Workman Publishing

Making Make-believe: Fun Props, Costumes and Creative Play Ideas; MaryAnn F. Kohl; Gryphon House

Games

Previous experience

Children's experiences in playing collaborative games will vary considerably, but most will have some experience of playing:

- circle time games;
- chanting games such as 'In and Out the Dusty Bluebells', 'What's the Time Mr Wolf?', 'The Farmer's in his Den';
- throwing and catching games;
- target games;
- simple board games.

The responsive adult

In the early stages of working with these materials it is crucial to continue to observe the children. Only by doing this can you set developmentally appropriate challenges and provocations. The ideas listed here are offered as suggestions; the most exciting challenges will arise from children's own interests and motivations,

which will only become apparent as you spend time with them, watching and joining them in their play. As you do this, you will be moving between the three interconnecting roles of observer, co-player, extender described below, and will be able to decide what you need to do next to take the learning forward. In three interconnecting roles, the responsive adult will be:

Observer

- observing
- listening
- interpreting

Co-player

- modelling
- playing alongside
- offering suggestions
- responding sensitively
- initiating with care!

Extender

- discussing ideas
- sharing thinking
- modelling new skills
- asking open questions
- being an informed extender
- instigating ideas and thoughts
- supporting children as they make links in learning
- making possibilities evident
- introducing new ideas and resources
- offering challenges and provocations

Offering challenges and provocations

In order to get the most out of games, children first need to build up a wide repertoire of different sorts of games. Once they have done this, they can innovate and make up new versions, using their creativity to invent and expand on their knowledge.

- Can you invent your own version of 'Snakes and Ladders' by painting or chalking the board on the ground?
- Find a beanbag and a piece of chalk. How many games can you invent, using this equipment?
- Find a wall, a piece of chalk and a ball. Can you invent a target game?
- Can you make a collection of games that can be played outside? Put them in a book. How can you make it easy to find the games in the book?

- Ask your parents and other family members to tell you about games they know. Add these to your book.
- Could you publish your book of games on the school website so other children can play them? You may need some help with this!
- Could you print your book and sell it to other schools?
- Here are some different sorts of games you could include:
  - games with trails
  - treasure hunts
  - games with bats and balls
  - games with beanbags
  - games with hoops
  - games with skittles
  - games with chalk
  - large board games
  - hopping, skipping and jumping games.

Ready for more?

♦ Find out about games from other cultures and countries. Try some of these games out.

♦ Interview some older people in the community or your grandparents. Find out what games they played when they were young. Try some of these.

♦ Can you make your own bats and balls from recycled materials? Find out how to make an elastic band ball.

♦ Find some empty plastic bottles. Fill them with water and use them to make your own skittles or a bowling alley.

♦ Make a game that is just about:

  • running

  • walking backwards with something on your head

  • lying down

  • finding things outside

  • some stones

  • different sorts of jumping.

♦ Make an obstacle race game. You can use some of these:

  • hoops

  • balls

  • dressing up clothes

  • beanbags

  • water

  • spoons.

♦ Invent some new games to be played in teams.

♦ Find out how to play Hopscotch.

♦ Invent a chanting game using names.

Materials

Educational suppliers and consortium groups have a huge range of equipment for game playing, but you could expand children's imaginative work in games by adding:

■ plastic containers of all sorts

■ chalk and other mark makers

■ planks, tyres, fabrics and cable reels

■ boxes, bags and baskets

■ recycled materials to make their own bats, balls, containers

■ old clothes, scarves, hats etc for dressing up games and relay races

■ jugs, bottles, plastic plates, chopsticks, to use with sand, water, stones etc.

It's important to give children plenty of time to work on their invented games, and to find some way of keeping track of their early efforts by photos or simple clipboard notes.

Materials, websites, books and other references

Websites

There are lots of sites with ring games, race games and other outdoor games - here are some:

web.ukonline.co.uk

www.gameskidsplay.net

en.wikipedia.org/wiki/Playground_game

www.freegames.eu.com

www.cheshire.gov.uk/ecoschools/Eco_Games - is a site that encourages children to invent their own games with sticks and other natural objects, or play the ones on the site.

Books

EarthFriendly Toys: Make Toys and Games from Reusable Objects (Earth-Friendly); George Pfiffner; Jossey Bass

Literacy 1 Speaking	• Retell stories, ordering events using story language • Tell stories and describe incidents from their own experience in an audible voice. • Interpret a text by reading aloud with some variety in pace and emphasis • Experiment with and build new stores of words to communicate in different contexts.	**Literacy 6** Word structure and spelling	• Spell new words using phonics as the prime approach • Segment sounds into their constituent phonemes in order to spell them correctly. Children move from spelling simple CVC words to longer words that include common diagraphs & adjacent consonants such as 'brush', 'crunch' • Recognise and use alternative ways of spelling the graphemes already taught, for example that the /ae/ sound can be spelt with 'ai', 'ay' or 'a-e'; that the /ee/ sound can also be spelt as 'ea' and 'e'; & begin to know which words contain which spelling alternatives • Use knowledge of common inflections in spelling, such as plurals, -ly, -er • Read and spell phonically decodable two and three syllable words.	**Literacy 8** Engaging and responding to text	• Select books for personal reading and give reasons for choices • Visualise and comment on events, characters and ideas, making imaginative links to their own experiences • Distinguish fiction and nonfiction texts and the different purposes for reading them.
Literacy 2 Listening and responding	• Listen with sustained concentration, building new stores of words in different contexts • Listen to tapes or video and express views about how a story or information has been presented • Listen to and follow instructions accurately, asking for help and clarification if necessary.			**Literacy 9** Creating and shaping texts	• Independently choose what to write about, plan and follow it through • Use key features of narrative in their own writing • Convey information and ideas in simple non-narrative forms • Find and use new and interesting words and phrases, including story language • Create short simple texts on paper and on screen that combine words with images (and sounds).
Literacy 3 Group discussion & interaction	• Take turns to speak, listen to others' suggestions and talk about what they are going to do • Ask and answer questions, make relevant contributions, offer suggestions and take turns • Explain their views to others in a small group, decide how to report the group's views to the class.	**Literacy 7** Understanding and interpreting texts	• Identify the main events and characters in stories, and find specific information in simple texts • Use syntax and context when reading for meaning • Make predictions showing an understanding of ideas, events and characters • Recognise the main elements that shape different texts • Explore the effect of patterns of language and repeated words and phrases.	**Literacy 10** Text structure and organisation	• Write chronological and non-chronological texts using simple structures • Group written sentences together in chunks of meaning or subject.
Literacy 4 Drama	• Explore familiar themes and characters through improvisation and role-play • Act out their own and well-known stories, using voices for characters • Discuss why they like a performance.			**Literacy 11** Sentence structure and punctuation	• Compose and write simple sentences independently to communicate meaning • Use capital letters and full stops when punctuating simple sentences.
Literacy 5 Word recognition, coding and decoding	• Recognise and use alternative ways of pronouncing the graphemes already taught, for example, that the grapheme 'g' is pronounced differently in 'get' and 'gem'; the grapheme 'ow' is pronounced differently in 'how' and 'show' • Recognise and use alternative ways of spelling the phonemes already taught, for example 'ae'' can be spelt with 'ai', 'ay' or 'a-e'; begin to know which words contain which spelling alternatives. • Identify the constituent parts of two-syllable and three-syllable words to support the application of phonic knowledge and skills. Recognise automatically an increasing number of familiar high frequency words		• Apply phonic knowledge and skills as the prime approach to reading and spelling unfamiliar words that are not completely decodable • Read more challenging texts which can be decoded using their acquired phonic knowledge and skills; automatic recognition of high frequency words. Read and spell phonically decodable two-syllable and three-syllable words.	**Literacy 12** Presentation	• Write most letters, correctly formed and orientated, using a comfortable and efficient pencil grip • Write with spaces between words accurately • Use the space bar and keyboard to type their name and simple texts.

Literacy 1
Speaking

- Speak with clarity and use appropriate intonation when reading and reciting texts
- Tell real and imagined stories using the conventions of familiar story language
- Explain ideas and processes using imaginative and adventurous vocabulary and nonverbal gestures to support communication

Literacy 2
Listening and responding

- Listen to others in class, ask relevant questions and follow instructions
- Listen to talk by an adult, remember some specific points and identify what they have learned
- Respond to presentations by describing characters, repeating some highlight and commenting constructively

Literacy 3
Group discussion and interaction

- Ensure that everyone contributes, allocate tasks, and consider alternatives and reach agreement
- Work effectively in groups by ensuring that each group member takes a turn challenging, supporting and moving on
- Listen to each other's views and preferences, agree the next steps to take and identify contributions by each group member

Literacy 4
Drama

- Adopt appropriate roles in small or large groups and consider alternative courses of action
- Present part of traditional stories, their own stories or work drawn from different parts of the curriculum for members of their own class
- Consider how mood and atmosphere are created in live or recorded performance

Literacy 5
Word recognition, coding and decoding

- Read independently and with increasing fluency longer and less familiar texts
- Spell with increasing accuracy and confidence, drawing on word recognition and knowledge of word structure, and spelling patterns
- Know how to tackle unfamiliar words that are not completely decodable
- Read and spell less common alternative graphemes including trigraphs
- Read high and medium frequency words independently and automatically

Literacy 6
Word structure and spelling

- Spell with increasing accuracy and confidence, drawing on word recognition and knowledge of word structure, and spelling patterns including common inflections and use of double letters
- Read and spell less common alternative graphemes including trigraphs

Literacy 7
Understanding and interpreting texts

- Draw together ideas and information from across a whole text, using simple signposts in the text
- Give reasons why things happen or characters change
- Explain organisational features of texts, including alphabetical order, layout, diagrams etc
- Use syntax and context to build their store of vocabulary when reading
- Explore how particular words are used, including words and expressions with similar meanings

Literacy 8
Engaging and responding to text

- Read whole books on their own, choosing and justifying selections
- Engage with books through exploring and enacting interpretations
- Explain their reactions to texts, commenting on important aspects

Literacy 9
Creating and shaping texts

- Draw on knowledge and experience of texts in deciding and planning what and how to write
- Sustain form in narrative, including use of person and time
- Maintain consistency in non-narrative, including purpose and tense
- Make adventurous word and language choices appropriate to the style and purpose of the text
- Select from different presentational features to suit particular writing purposes on paper and on screen

Literacy 10
Text structure and organisation

- Use planning to establish clear sections for writing
- Use appropriate language to make sections hang together

Literacy 11
Sentence structure and punctuation

- Write simple and compound sentences and begin to use subordination in relation to time and reason
- Compose sentences using tense consistently (present and past)
- Use question marks, and use commas to separate items in a list

Literacy 12
Presentation

- Write legibly, using upper and lower case letters appropriately within words, and observing correct spacing within and between words
- Form and use the four basic handwriting joins
- Word process short narrative and non-narrative texts

Mathematics 1 Using and applying maths	• Solve problems involving counting, adding, subtracting, doubling or halving in the context of numbers, measures or money, for example to 'pay' and 'give change' • Describe a puzzle or problem using numbers, practical materials and diagrams; use these to solve the problem and set the solution in the original context • Answer a question by selecting and using suitable equipment, and sorting information, shapes or objects; display results using tables and pictures • Describe simple patterns and relationships involving numbers or shapes; decide whether examples satisfy given conditions • Describe ways of solving puzzles and problems, explaining choices and decisions orally or using pictures	**Mathematics 4** Calculating	• Relate addition to counting on; recognise that addition can be done in any order; use practical and informal written methods to support the addition of a one-digit number or a multiple of 10 to a one-digit or two- digit number • Understand subtraction as 'take away' and find a 'difference' by counting up; use practical and informal written methods to support the subtraction of a one-digit number from a one-digit or two digit number and a multiple of 10 from a two- digit number • Solve practical problems that involve combining groups of 2, 5 or 10, or sharing into equal groups • Use the vocabulary related to addition and subtraction and symbols to describe and record addition and subtraction number sentences
Mathematics 2 Counting and understanding numbers	• Count reliably at least 20 objects, recognising that when rearranged the number of objects stays the same; estimate a number of objects that can be checked by counting • Compare and order numbers, using the related vocabulary; use the equals (=) sign • Read and write numerals from 0 to 20, then beyond; use knowledge of place value to position these numbers on a number track and number line • Say the number that is 1 more or less than any given number, and 10 more or less for multiples of 10 • Use the vocabulary of halves and quarters in context	**Mathematics 5** Understanding shape	• Visualise and name common 2-D shapes and 3-D solids and describe their features; use them to make patterns, pictures and models • Identify objects that turn about a point (e.g. scissors) or about a line (e.g. a door); recognise and make whole, half and quarter turns • Visualise and use everyday language to describe the position of objects and direction and distance when moving them, for example when placing or moving objects on a game board
		Mathematics 6 Measuring	• Estimate, measure, weigh and compare objects, choosing and using suitable uniform non-standard or standard units and measuring instruments (e.g. a lever balance, metre stick or measuring jug) • Use vocabulary related to time; order days of the week and months; read the time to the hour and half hour
Mathematics 3 Knowing and using number facts	• Derive and recall all pairs of numbers with a total of 10 and addition facts for totals to at least 5; work out the corresponding subtraction facts • Count on or back in ones, twos, fives and tens and use this knowledge to derive the multiples of 2, 5 and 10 to the tenth multiple • Recall the doubles of all numbers to at least 10	**Mathematics 7** Handling data	• Answer a question by recording information in lists and tables; present outcomes using practical resources, pictures, block graphs or pictograms • Use diagrams to sort objects into groups according to a given criterion; suggest a different criterion for grouping the same objects

Mathematics 1

Using and applying maths

- Solve problems involving addition, subtraction, multiplication or division in contexts of numbers, measures or pounds and pence
- Identify and record the information or calculation needed to solve a puzzle or problem; carry out the steps or calculations and check the solution in the context of the problem
- Follow a line of enquiry; answer questions by choosing and using suitable equipment and selecting, organising and presenting information in lists, tables and simple diagrams
- Describe patterns and relationships involving numbers or shapes, make predictions and test these with examples
- Present solutions to puzzles and problems in an organised way; explain decisions, methods and results in pictorial, spoken or written form, using mathematical language and number sentences

Mathematics 2

Counting and understanding numbers

- Read and write two-digit and three-digit numbers in figures and words; describe and extend number sequences and recognise odd and even numbers
- Count up to 100 objects by grouping them and counting in tens, fives or twos; explain what each digit in a two-digit number represents, including numbers where 0 is a place holder; partition two-digit numbers in different ways, including into multiples of 10 and 1
- Order two-digit numbers and position them on a number line; use the greater than (>) and less than (<) signs
- Estimate a number of objects; round two-digit numbers to the nearest 10
- Find one half, one quarter and three quarters of shapes and sets of objects

Mathematics 3

Knowing and using number facts

- Derive and recall all addition and subtraction facts for each number to at least 10, all pairs with totals to 20 and all pairs of multiples of 10 with totals up to 100
- Understand that halving is the inverse of doubling and derive and recall doubles of all numbers to 20, and the corresponding halves
- Derive and recall multiplication facts for the 2, 5 and 10 times-tables and the related division facts; recognise multiples of 2, 5 and 10
- Use knowledge of number facts and operations to estimate and check answers to calculations

Mathematics 4

Calculating

- Add or subtract mentally a one-digit number or a multiple of 10 to or from any two-digit number; use practical and informal written methods to add and subtract two-digit numbers
- Understand that subtraction is the inverse of addition and vice versa; use this to derive and record related addition and subtraction number sentences
- Represent repeated addition and arrays as multiplication, and sharing and repeated subtraction (grouping) as division; use practical and informal written methods and related vocabulary to support multiplication and division, including calculations with remainders
- Use the symbols $+$, $-$, $?$, $\div$ and $=$ to record and interpret number sentences involving all four operations; calculate the value of an unknown in a number sentence (e.g. $\square \div 2 = 60$, $30 - \square = 24$).

Mathematics 5

Understanding shape

- Visualise common 2-D shapes and 3-D solids; identify shapes from pictures of them in different positions and orientations; sort, make and describe shapes, referring to their properties
- Identify reflective symmetry in patterns and 2-D shapes and draw lines of symmetry in shapes
- Follow and give instructions involving position, direction and movement
- Recognise and use whole, half and quarter turns, both clockwise and anticlockwise; know that a right angle represents a quarter turn

Mathematics 6

Measuring

- Estimate, compare & measure lengths, weights and capacities, choosing & using standard units (m, cm, kg, litre) & suitable measuring instruments
- Read the numbered divisions on a scale, and interpret the divisions between them (e.g. on a scale from 0 to 25 with intervals of 1 shown but only the divisions 0, 5, 10, 15 and 20 numbered); use a ruler to draw and measure lines to the nearest centimetre
- Use units of time (seconds, minutes, hours, days) and know the relationships between them; read the time to the quarter hour; identify time intervals, including those that cross the hour

Mathematics 7

Handling data

- Answer a question by collecting and recording data in lists and tables; represent the data as block graphs or pictograms to show results; use ICT to organise and present data
- Use lists, tables and diagrams to sort objects; explain choices using appropriate language, including 'not'

KS1 Programme of Study for Key Stage 1: Science

SC1 Scientific enquiry

Sc 1.1	1.1a	1.1b	1.1c	1.1d
Planning	Ask questions 'How?', 'Why?', 'What if?' and decide how they might find answers to them	Use first-hand experience and simple information sources to answer questions	Think about what might happen before deciding what to do	Recognise when a test or comparison is unfair
Sc 1.2	**1.2a**	**1.2b**	**1.2c**	**1.2d**
Ideas and evidence, collecting evidence	Follow simple instructions to control the risks to themselves and to others	Explore using the senses of sight, hearing, smell, touch and taste as appropriate. Make and record observations and measurements	Communicate what happened in a variety of ways including using ICT	
Sc 1.3	**1.3a**	**1.3b**	**1.3c**	**1.3d**
Comparing evidence	Make simple comparisons (eg, hand span, shoe size) and identify simple patterns or associations, and try to explain it, drawing on their knowledge and understanding	Compare what happened with what they expected would happen and try to explain it. Draw on their knowledge and understanding	Review their work and explain what they did to others	

SC2 Life processes and living things

Sc 2.1	2.1a	2.1b	2.1c	2.1d
Life processes	Differences between things that are living and things that have never been alive	That animals, including humans, move, feed, grow, use their senses and reproduce	Relate life processes to animals and plants found in the local environment	
Sc 2.2	**2.2a**	**2.2b**	**2.2c**	**2.2d**
Ideas and evidence, collecting evidence	Recognise and compare the main external parts of the bodies of humans and other animals	That humans and other animals need food and water to stay alive	That taking exercise and eating the right types and amounts of food help humans to keep healthy	About the role of drugs as medicines
	2.2e	**2.2f**	**2.2g**	
	How to treat animals with care and sensitivity	That humans and other animals can produce off-spring and these off-spring grow into adults	About the senses that enable humans and other animals to be aware of the world around them	
Sc 2.3	**2.3a**	**2.3b**	**2.3c**	**2.3d**
Green plants	Recognise that plants need light and water to grow	To recognise and name the leaf, flowers, stem and root of flowering plants	That seeds grow into flowering plants	
Sc 2.4	**2.4a**	**2.4b**		
Variation and classification	Recognise similarities and differences between themselves and others, and to treat others with sensitivity	Group living things according to observable similarities and differences		
Sc 2.5	**2.5a**	**2.5b**	**2.5c**	
Living things in their environment	Find out about the different kinds of plants and animals in the local environment	Identify similarities & differences between local environments & ways in which these affect animals & plants that are found there	Care for the environment	

SC3 Materials and their properties

Sc 3.1	3.1a	3.1b	3.1c	3.1d
Grouping materials	Use their senses to explore and recognise the similarities and differences between materials	Sort objects into groups on the basis of their properties: texture, float, hardness and transparency and whether they are magnetic or non-magnetic	Recognise and name common types of material and recognise that some of them are found naturally	Find out about the uses of a variety of materials and how these are chosen for specific uses on the basis of their simple properties

Sc 3.2	3.2a	3.2b		
Changing materials	Find out how the shapes of objects made from some materials can be changed by some processes including squashing, bending, twisting and stretching	Explore and describe the way some everyday materials, e.g. water, chocolate, bread and clay, change when they are heated or cooled		

SC4 Physical processes

Sc 4.1	4.1a	4.1b	4.1c	4.1d
Electricity	About everyday appliances that use electricity	Simple series circuits involving batteries, wires, bulbs and other components e.g. buzzers	How a switch can be used to break a circuit	Recognise when a test or comparison is unfair

Sc 4.2	4.2a	4.2b	4.2c	
Forces and motion	Find out about and describe the movement of familiar things e.g. cars going faster, slowing down, changing direction	That both pushes and pulls are examples of forces	To recognise that when things speed up, slow down, or change direction there is a cause	

Sc 4.3	4.3a	4.3b	4.3c	4.3d
Light and sound	Identify different light sources including the sun	That darkness is the absence of light	That there are many kinds of sound and sources of sound	That sounds travel away from sources, getting fainter as they do so, and that they are heard

KS1 Programmes of Study

History

H 1	1a	1b	1c
Chronological understanding	Place events and objects in chronological order	Use common words and phrases relating to the passing of time e.g. before, after, a long time ago and past	Retrieve information that has been stored
H 2	**2a**	**2b**	
Knowledge & understanding of events people and changes	Recognise why people did things, why events happened and what happened as a result	Identify differences between ways of life at different times	
H 3	**3a**		
Historical interpretation	Identify different ways in which the past is represented		
H 4	**4a**	**4b**	
Historical enquiry	Find out about the past from a range of sources of information	Ask and answer questions about the past	
H 5	**5a**		
Organisation and communication	Select from their knowledge of history and communicate it in a variety of ways		
H 6	**6a**	**6b**	**6c**	**6d**
Breadth of study	Changes in their own lives and the way of life of their family or others around them	The way of life of people in the more distant past who lived in the local area or elsewhere in Britain	The lives of significant men, women or children	Past events from the history of Britain and the wider world

Design and Technology

D&T 1	1a	1b	1c	1d	1e
Developing, planning and communicating ideas	Generate ideas by drawing on their own and other people's experiences	Develop ideas by hoping materials and putting together components	Talk about their ideas	Plan by suggesting what to do next as their ideas develop	Communicate ideas using a variety of materials including drawing and making moulds
D&T 2	**2a**	**2b**	**2c**	**2d**	**2e**
Working with tools, equipment and materials	Explore sensory qualities of materials	Measure, mark out, cut and shape	Assemble, join and combine materials	Use simple finishing techniques	Follow safe procedures
D&T 3	**3a**	**3b**			
Evaluating processes and products	Talk about their ideas	Identify improvements			
D&T 4	**4a**	**4b**			
Knowledge & understanding of materials and components	Working characteristics of materials	How mechanisms can be used			
D&T 5	**5a**	**5b**	**5c**		
Breadth of study	Focused practical tasks	Design and make assignments	Investigate and evaluate products		

Geography

G 1.1	1.1a	1.1b	1.1c	1.1d	
Geographical enquiry	Ask geographical questions	Observe and record	Express their own views about people, places, and environments	Communicate in different ways	

G 1.2	1.2a	1.2b	1.2c	1.2d	
Geographical skills	Use geographical vocabulary	Use fieldwork skills	Use globes, maps and plans at a range of scales	Use secondary sources of information	

G 2	2a	2b	2c	2d	2e
Knowledge and understanding of places	Identify and describe what places are like	Identify and describe what places are	Recognise how places become they way they are & how they are changing	Recognise how places compare with other places	Recognise how places are linked to other places in the world

G 3	3a	3b	3c	3d	
Knowledge & understanding of patterns & processes	Make observations about where things are located	Recognise changes in physical & human features			

G 4	4a	4b			
Knowledge & understanding of environment	Recognise changes in the environment	Recognise how the environment may be improved & sustained			

G 5	5a	5b	5c	5d	
Breadth of study	The locality of the school	A contrasting locality in the UK or overseas	Study at a local scale	Carry out fieldwork investigations outside the classroom	

ICT

ICT 1.1	1.1a	1.1b	1.1c	1.1d
Finding things out	Gather information from a variety of sources	Enter and store information in a variety of forms	Retrieve information that has been stored	

ICT 1.2	1.2a	1.2b	1.2c	1.2d
Developing ideas and making things happen	Use text, tables, images and sound to develop their ideas	Select from and add to information thay have rerieved for particular purposes	Plan and give instructions to make things happen	Try things out and explore what happens in real and imaginary instructions

ICT 2	2a	2b		
Exchanging and sharing information	Share their ideas by presenting information in a variety of forms	Present their completed work effectively		

Physical Education

PE 1	1a	1b	
Aquiring and developing skills	Explore basic skills, actions and ideas with increasing understanding	Remember and repeat simple skills & actions with increasing control	

PE 2	2a	2b	2c
Selecting and applying skills, tactics and compositional ideas	Explore how to choose and apply skills and actions in sequence & in combination	Vary the way they perform skills by using simple tactics and movement phrases	Apply rules and conventions for different activities

PE 3	3a	3b	3c
Evaluating and improving performance	Describe what they have done	Observe, describe & copy what others have done	Use what they have learnt to improve the quality and control of their work

PE 4	4a	4b	
Knowledge and understanding of fitness and health	How important it is to be active	Recognise and describe how their bodies feel during different activities	

PE 5	5a	5b	5c
Breadth of study	Dance	Games	Gymnastics

Art and Design

A&D 1	1a	1b		
Exploring and developing ideas	Record from first hand observation, experience & imagination	Ask and answer questions about the starting points for their work		

A&D 2	2a	2b	2c	
Investigating and making art, craft and design	Investigate the possibilities of materials and processes	Try out tools and techniques and apply these	Represent observations, ideas and feelings	

A&D 3	3a	3b		
Evaluating and developing work	Review what they and others have done	Identify what they might change		

A&D 4	4a	4b	4c	
Knowledge and understanding of materials and components	Visual and tactile elements	Materials and processes used in making art, craft and design	Differences and similarities in the work of artists, craftspeople and designers	

A&D 5	5a	5b	5c	5d
Breadth of study	Exploring a range of starting points	Working on their own and collaborating with others	Using a range of materials and processes	Investigating different types of art, craft and design

Music

M 1	1a	1b	1c	
Performing skills	Use their voices expressively by singing songs, chants, rhymes	Play tuned and untuned instruments	Rehearse and perform with others	

M 2	2a	2b		
Composing skills	Create musical patterns	Explore, choose and organise sounds and musical ideas		

M 3	3a	3b		
Responding and reviewing — appraising skills	Explore and express their ideas and feelings about music	Make improvements to their own work		

M 4	4a	4b	4c	
Responding and reviewing — listening skills	Listen with concentration and internalise & recall sounds	How combined musical elements can be organised	How sounds can be made in different ways	

M 5	5a	5b	5c	5d
Breadth of study	A range of musical activities	Responding to a range of starting points	Working on their own, in groups and as a class	A range of live and recorded music

PSHE: non-statutory guidance

PSHE 1	1a	1b	1c	1d	1e			
Developing confidence & responsibility & making the most of their abilities	Recognise their likes and dislikes, what is fair and unfair, what is right and wrong	Share their opinions on things that matter to them and their views	Recognise, name and deal with their feelings in a positive way	Think about themselves, learn from their experiences and recognise what they are good at	How to set simple goals			

PSHE 2	2a	2b	2c	2d	2e	2f	2g	
Preparing to play an active role as citizens	Take part in discussions with one other person and the whole class	Take part in a simple debate about topical issues	Recognise choices they make, and the difference between right and wrong	Realise that people and other living things have needs, and that they have responsibilities to meet them	That they belong to various groups and communities, such as a family	What improves and harms their local, natural & built environments	Contribute to the life of the class and school	Realise that money comes from different sources

PSHE 3	3a	3b	3c	3d	3e	3f	3g	
Developing a healthier lifestyle	Make simple choices that improve their health and wellbeing	Maintain personal hygiene	How some diseases spread and can be controlled	About the process of growing from young to old and how people's needs change	Name the main parts of the body	That household products and medicines can be harmful	Rules for, and ways of, keeping safe, basic road safety	

PSHE 4	4a	4b	4c	4d	4e			
Developing good relationships and respecting differences	Recognise how their behaviour affects other people	Listen to other people and play and work co-operatively	Identify and respect differences and similarities between people	That family and friends should care for each other	That there are different types of teasing and bullying, that bullying is wrong